Answers: P.1 — P.10

Section One

Types of Number P.1

Q1 4 (or -4)

Q2 -3 °C

Q3 The third cube number (27)

Q4 81, 121, 169, 225

Q5 **a)** All of them
b) 17, 9123, 5, 42, 85, 33, 12.00, 100 000
c) 17, -4, 0, 9123, 5, -9123, 42, 85, 33, 12.00, 100 000

Q6 Rational, e.g. 3.14, irrational, e.g. π

Q7 **a)** $\sqrt{2} \times \sqrt{8}$, $(\sqrt{5})^6$, 0.4, $40 - 2^{-1} - 4^{-2}$, $49^{-1/2}$
b) $\sqrt{3} \div \sqrt{2}$, $(\sqrt{7})^3$, 6π, $\sqrt{5} - 2.1$, $\sqrt{6} - 6$

Multiples, Factors and Primes P.2-P.3

Q1 **a)** 12   **d)** 1, 3, 9
b) 3   **e)** P = 12, Q = 6
c) 1, 9

Q2 The Conversational French and Woodturning classes both have a prime number of pupils and so cannot be divided into equal groups.

Q3 **a)** 1, 8, 27, 64, 125   **d)** 8, 64
b) 8, 64   **e)** 125
c) 27

Q4 **a)** 2
b) E.g. 29, 59, 251, 521, etc.
c) 19
d) 2 and 19
e) E.g. 1, 12, 15, 21, 25, 51, 52, 92, etc.

Q5 293

Q6 1

Q7 42

Q8 **a)** 6, 12, 18, 24, 30, 36, 42, 48, 54, 60
b) 5, 10, 15, 20, 25, 30, 35, 40, 45, 50
c) 30

Q9 **a)** 1, 2, 3, 5, 6, 10, 15, 30
b) 1, 2, 3, 4, 6, 8, 12, 16, 24, 48
c) 6

Q10 **a)** 20   **f)** 5
b) 10   **g)** 32
c) 2   **h)** 16
d) 15   **i)** 16
e) 15

Q11 **a)** 120   **f)** 180
b) 120   **g)** 64
c) 120   **h)** 192
d) 45   **i)** 192
e) 90

Q12 **a)** 7th June   **c)** Sunday (1st July)
b) 16th June   **d)** Lars

Square and Cube Roots P.4

Q1 **a)** 8   **g)** 27
b) 4   **h)** 1
c) 6   **i)** 13
d) 14   **j)** 85
e) 23   **k)** 1000
f) 9   **l)** 5

Q2 **a)** 2, -2   **f)** 10, -10
b) 4, -4   **g)** 12, -12
c) 3, -3   **h)** 8, -8
d) 7, -7   **i)** 9, -9
e) 5, -5

Q3 **a)** 16   **d)** 100
b) 12   **e)** 1
c) 11   **f)** 0.5

Q4 **a)** 4   **d)** 10
b) 8   **e)** 6
c) 5   **f)** 20

Q5 7 cm

Q6 240 m

Order of Operations P.5

Q1 **a)** 8   **f)** 319.98
b) 5   **g)** 5.5
c) 6.56   **h)** 983
d) 11.22   **i)** 9.17
e) -0.9   **j)** 0

Q2 **a)** 8   **f)** 8.67
b) 73   **g)** 1
c) 113   **h)** 1.42
d) 7   **i)** -488.76
e) 22.57   **j)** -0.26

Q3 **a)** 3   **g)** -176.95
b) 0.1   **h)** 0.21
c) 16   **i)** 0.58
d) 8.33   **j)** 0.27
e) -0.01   **k)** 0.01
f) 70.88   **l)** -10.64

Calculator Buttons P.6-P.7

Q1 **a)** 1   **f)** 900
b) 4   **g)** 25
c) 121   **h)** 1 000 000
d) 256   **i)** 0
e) 1

Q2 **a)** 4   **f)** 20
b) 6   **g)** 1.73
c) 17   **h)** 2.65
d) 0   **i)** 5.48
e) 60

Q3 **a)** 1   **e)** 3
b) 0   **f)** -3
c) 7   **g)** -4
d) 10   **h)** -1.71

Q4 **a)** 8.4   **d)** 3.4
b) 0.0017   **e)** 0.87
c) 0.66   **f)** 1.17

Q5 **a)** i) $\frac{1}{3}$ ii) $\frac{8}{13}$ iii) $\frac{1}{8}$
b) i) $3\frac{2}{5}$ ii) $9\frac{7}{24}$ iii) $45\frac{14}{107}$
c) i) $\frac{7}{3}$ ii) $\frac{195}{23}$ iii) $\frac{2635}{63}$

Q6 **a)** 2   **d)** 29.87
b) 1   **e)** 0.35
c) 0.33   **f)** 0.07

Q7 **a)** 1   **f)** 59049
b) 1048576   **g)** 0.49 (to 2 d.p.)
c) 1048576   **h)** 26742.44 (to 2 d.p.)
d) 9.87   **i)** 0.25
e) 0.5

Q8 **a)** 4000   **c)** 620 000
b) 10 000

Q9 **a)** 4   **d)** 0.05
b) 0.2   **e)** 0.02
c) 2   **f)** 400

Standard Form P.8-P.9

Q1 **a)** 35.6   **g)** 0.82
b) 3560   **h)** 0.0082
c) 0.356   **i)** 1570
d) 35600   **j)** 0.157
e) 8.2   **k)** 157000
f) 0.00082   **l)** 15.7

Q2 **a)** 2.56×10^0 **g)** 9.52×10^4
b) 2.56×10 **h)** 9.52×10^{-4}
c) 2.56×10^{-1} **i)** 4.2×10^3
d) 2.56×10^4 **j)** 4.2×10^{-3}
e) 9.52×10 **k)** 4.2×10
f) 9.52×10^{-2} **l)** 4.2×10^2

Q3 **a)** 3.47×10^2 **g)** 7.5×10^{-5}
b) 7.3004×10 **h)** 5×10^{-4}
c) 5×10^0 **i)** 5.34×10^0
d) 9.183×10^5 **j)** 6.2103×10^2
e) 1.5×10^7 **k)** 1.49×10^4
f) 9.371×10^6 **l)** 3×10^{-7}

Q4 **a)** 6×10^{-3} mm
b) 1×10^9
c) 1×10^{12}
d) 9.46×10^{12} km
e) 6.9138×10^4 miles

Q5 1.2×10^{-2} mm

Q6 **a)** Mercury   **b)** Jupiter
c) Mercury   **d)** Neptune
e) Mercury, Venus
f) Jupiter, Neptune, Saturn

Q7 **a)** 2.4×10^{10} **b)** 1.6×10^6
c) 1.8×10^5

Q8 1.04×10^{13} is greater by 5.78×10^{12}

Q9 1.3×10^{-9} is smaller by 3.07×10^{-8}

Q10 **a)** 4.2×10^7 **f)** 4.232×10^{-3}
b) 3.8×10^{-4} **g)** 1.7×10^{18}
c) 1×10^7 **h)** 2.83×10^{-4}
d) 1.12×10^{-4} **i)** 1×10^{-2}
e) 8.43×10^5

Q11 7×10^6

Q12 6.38×10^8 cm

Q13 3.222×10^{-27} kg

Q14 **a)** 1.8922×10^{16} m
b) 4.7305×10^{15} m

Q15 **a)** 510 000 000 km²
b) 3.62×10^8 km²
c) 148 000 000 km²

Sets P.10-P.11

Q1 **a)** E = {prime numbers less than 12}
b) E = {2, 3, 5, 7, 11}

Q2 **a)** L   **b)** 10
c) E.g. $1 \in K$ and $1.1 \notin K$

Q3 **a)** B = {-3, 1, 7, 8, 9, 12, 21}
b)

Q4 **a)** R = {1, 8, 27, 64}
b) n(S) = 9
c) R ∩ S = {1, 64}
d) n(R ∪ S) = 11

Answers: P.11 — P.17

Q5   **a)** People who answered the survey
    b) 9
    c) n(D ∪ P) = 58 and n(D ∩ P) = 3

Q6   **a)**

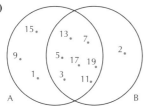

    b)

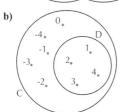

Q7   **a)** false   **g)** true
    b) false   **h)** false
    c) true   **i)** true
    d) false   **j)** false
    e) false   **k)** true
    f) false   **l)** false

Q8   **a)** All the cows he counted
    b) 19
    c) n(P) = 83
    d) n(C ∪ G) = 59
    e) n(C') = 80
    f) n(C ∩ P) = 25
    g) n(C ∩ G ∩ P) = 11
    h) n(G ∩ P ∪ C') = 23

Section Two

Fractions, Decimals and Percentages P.12-P.13

Q1   **a)** 25%   **e)** 41.52%
    b) 50%   **f)** 84.06%
    c) 75%   **g)** 39.62%
    d) 10%   **h)** 28.28%

Q2   **a)** 0.5   **e)** 0.602
    b) 0.12   **f)** 0.549
    c) 0.4   **g)** 0.431
    d) 0.34   **h)** 0.788

Q3   **a)** 50%   **e)** 4%
    b) 25%   **f)** 66.7%
    c) 12.5%   **g)** 26.7%
    d) 75%   **h)** 28.6%

Q4   **a)** $\frac{1}{4}$ **e)** $\frac{41}{500}$
    b) $\frac{3}{5}$ **f)** $\frac{62}{125}$
    c) $\frac{9}{20}$ **g)** $\frac{443}{500}$
    d) $\frac{3}{10}$ **h)** $\frac{81}{250}$

Q5   85%

Q6   C

Q7   **a)** 0.3   **e)** 1.75
    b) 0.37   **f)** 0.125
    c) 0.4   **g)** 0.6
    d) 0.375   **h)** 0.05

Q8

Fraction	Decimal
$\frac{1}{2}$	0.5
$\frac{1}{5}$	0.2
$\frac{1}{8}$	0.125
$\frac{8}{5}$	1.6
$\frac{4}{16}$	0.25
$\frac{7}{2}$	3.5
$\frac{x}{10}$	0.x
$\frac{x}{100}$	0.0x
$\frac{3}{20}$	0.15
$\frac{9}{20}$	0.45

Q9   **a)** $0.8\dot{3}$ **e)** $0.\dot{9}0$
    b) $0.\dot{7}$ **f)** $0.\dot{4}6031\dot{7}$
    c) $0.6\dot{3}$ **g)** $0.\dot{4}7\dot{8}$
    d) $0.4\dot{7}$ **h)** $0.\dot{5}89\dot{1}$

Q10   **a)** $\frac{3}{5}$ **e)** $\frac{1}{3}$
    b) $\frac{3}{4}$ **f)** $\frac{2}{3}$
    c) $\frac{19}{20}$ **g)** $\frac{1}{9}$
    d) $\frac{16}{125}$ **h)** $\frac{1}{6}$

Q11   **a)** $\frac{2}{9}$ **e)** $\frac{4}{33}$
    b) $\frac{4}{9}$ **f)** $\frac{545}{999}$
    c) $\frac{8}{9}$ **g)** $\frac{251}{333}$
    d) $\frac{80}{99}$ **h)** $\frac{52}{333}$

Fractions P.14-P.16

Q1   **a)** $\frac{1}{64}$ **d)** $3\frac{29}{32}$
    b) $\frac{1}{9}$ **e)** $5\frac{5}{32}$
    c) $\frac{1}{18}$ **f)** $\frac{81}{100000}$

Q2   **a)** 1   **d)** $\frac{2}{5}$
    b) 4   **e)** $\frac{10}{33}$
    c) $\frac{1}{2}$ **f)** 1000

Q3   **a)** $\frac{1}{4}$ **d)** $4\frac{3}{8}$
    b) $\frac{5}{6}$ **e)** $5\frac{3}{8}$
    c) $\frac{1}{2}$ **f)** 1

Q4   Yes (she makes $3\frac{7}{15}$ litres of punch).

Q5   **a)** 0   **d)** $1\frac{7}{8}$
    b) $\frac{1}{2}$ **e)** $-2\frac{7}{8}$
    c) $-\frac{1}{6}$ **f)** $\frac{4}{5}$

Q6   **a)** $\frac{3}{4}$ **g)** $\frac{5}{8}$
    b) $\frac{5}{12}$ **h)** $-\frac{1}{24}$
    c) $\frac{7}{15}$ **i)** $4\frac{3}{5}$
    d) $4\frac{3}{4}$ **j)** $1\frac{1}{30}$
    e) 4   **k)** 1
    f) $1\frac{1}{5}$ **l)** $\frac{44}{75}$

Q7   **a)** $\frac{1}{12}$ **b)** $\frac{1}{4}$ **c)** $\frac{2}{3}$

Q8   **a)** $\frac{3}{4}$ **b)** $\frac{5}{8}$ **c)** $\frac{1}{8}$

Q9   Kitchen staff — $\frac{3}{5}$ girls

    Employees — $\frac{2}{5}$ boys

Q10 $\frac{7}{30}$ offered no opinion

Q11   **a)** $\frac{2}{5}$ of the days in November

    b) 6 days

Q12   **a)** Each box will hold 16 sandwiches. So 5 boxes will be needed for 80 sandwiches.
    b) 25 inches tall

Q13   **a)** $\frac{1}{18}$ live in Perth

    b) $\frac{1}{4}$ live in either Perth or Sydney

Q14   **a)** 48 km²

    b) $\frac{5}{8}$ of the total area

Q15   **a)** 8 chose other vegetables

    b) $\frac{7}{20}$ chose carrots

    c) $\frac{1}{4}$ chose peas

    d) At least 57 people

    e) Not more than 65 people

Q16 $1\frac{7}{9}$ m

Q17   **a)** 100 g   **c)** $\frac{2}{7}$ is flour
    b) 350 g   **d)** 300 g

Q18   £31.07

Multiplying and Dividing Decimals P.17

Q1   **a)** 2.52   **e)** 88.92
    b) 17.1   **f)** 101.53
    c) 36.27   **g)** 369.46
    d) 28.5   **h)** 25245.02

Q2   **a)** 231   **e)** 8
    b) 64   **f)** 31.75
    c) 39   **g)** 5.75
    d) 0.5   **h)** 0.75

Q3   **a)** 6   **b)** £2.46

Q4   **a)** and **b)**

Ingredient	Amount	Cost
Sugar	0.9 kg	£1.35
Butter	0.9 kg	£3.96
Flour	1.05 kg	£1.26
Eggs	15	£3.40
Milk	0.12 l	£0.10
Vanilla	22.5 ml	£0.54

Total cost: £10.61

Q5   **a)** 8.2 m/s   **c)** 49 m
    b) 1.9 s   **d)** 5.1

Answers: P.18 — P.28

Speed, Distance and Time P.18-P.19

Q1 60 km/h
Q2 165 km
Q3 2 hrs 40 mins
Q4

Distance Travelled	Time Taken	Average Speed
210 km	3 hrs	70 km/h
135 km	4 hrs 30 mins	30 km/h
105 km	2 hrs 30 mins	42 km/h
9 km	45 mins	12 km/h
640 km	48 mins	800 km/h
70 km	1 hr 10 mins	60 km/h

Q5 a) 9.1 m/s   b) 32.7 km/h
Q6 540 km/h
Q7 Journey takes 3 hrs 39 mins.
07.05 to 10.30 is 3 hrs 25 mins.
So Pete will not be in London on time.
Q8 a) 98.9 km/h
b) 72.56 s   c) 99.2 km/h
Q9 a) 5 hrs 31 mins 30 s
b) 405 km   c) 73.3 km/h
Q10 2.15 pm
Q11 a) 2 hrs 14 mins
b) 1 hr 59 mins   c) 1346 and 1401
Q12 16 km/h is faster. 38 and 42 mins.
Q13 a) 488 km
b) 920.8 km   c) 497 km/h
Q14 a) 8.1 m/s   b) 7.3 m/s
Q15 a) 220 km
b) 5 mins 4 s (to the nearest second)
Q16 1 hr 27 mins
Q17 a) 4.8 m/s
b) 14.4 m/s
c) 14.4 m/s
d) 17.3 km/h, 51.8 km/h
Q18 122.7 s, 124.2 s and 127.7 s

Ratios P.20-P.21

Q1 a) 3:4   d) 9:16
b) 1:4   e) 7:2
c) 1:2   f) 9:1
Q2 a) 6 cm   d) 1.5 cm
b) 11 cm   e) 2.75 cm
c) 30.4 m   f) 7.6 m
Q3 a) £8 and £12
b) 80 m and 70 m
c) 100 g, 200 g and 200 g
d) 1 h 20 m, 2 h 40 m and 4 hrs
Q4 4 and 12 squares
Q5 400 ml, 600 ml and 1000 ml
Q6 Jane £40, Holly £48 and Rose £12
Q7 Paul, £16
Q8 a) $\frac{1}{2}$ b) $\frac{3}{10}$
Q9 a) 245   b) 210
Q10 a) 54.00   b) 80 cm
Q11 30
Q12 a) £39   b) £140
Q13 a) 1:300
b) 6 m   c) 3.33 cm
Q14 a) 15 kg
b) 30 kg
c) 8 kg cement, 24 kg sand, 48 kg gravel

Q15 a) 30
b) 15   c) $\frac{2}{3}$
Q16 a) 45   b) 90

Proportion P.22

Q1 85
Q2 £247.80
Q3 112 hrs
Q4 £96.10
Q5 96 sheep
Q6 a) 9.33 cm
b) 30.45 km
Q7 44 cows
Q8 a) 320
b) 560   c) 880
Q9 a) 55.3 cm   c) 20.4°C
b) 51.5 cm   d) 19.5°C
Q10 a) 199 500 km/s
b) 123 657 km/s
c) 299 250 km/s

Percentages P.23-P.25

Q1 a) 0.2   c) 0.02
b) 0.35   d) 0.625
Q2 a) $\frac{1}{5}$
b) $\frac{3}{100}$
c) $\frac{7}{10}$
d) $\frac{421}{500}$
Q3 a) 12.5%   c) 30%
b) 23%   d) 34%
Q4 85%
Q5 72.5%
Q6 £351.33
Q7 £244.40
Q8 23 028
Q9 a) £4275
b) £6840
Q10 Car 1 costs £8495 × 0.85 = £7220.75
Car 2 costs £8195 × 0.88 = £7211.60
So car 2 is the cheaper.
Q11 a) £5980
b) £5501.60
Q12 Total cost is £152.75. Can't afford it.
Q13 31%
Q14 13%
Q15 1.6%
Q16 500%
Q17 a) 67.7%
b) 93.5%
c) 38.1%
Q18 a) £236.25
b) £225.04
c) £255.34
Q19 38%
Q20 £80
Q21 a) 300   b) 4 years

Time P.26

Q1 a) 5 am   d) 3.58 pm
b) 2.48 pm   e) 10.30 pm
c) 3.16 am   f) 12.01 am
Q2 a) 2330   d) 1215
b) 1022   e) 0830
c) 0015   f) 1645
Q3 145 mins
Q4 a) 8 hours
b) 10 hours
c) 11 hrs 56 mins
d) 47 hrs 48 mins
Q5 a) 3 hrs 15 mins
b) 24 mins
c) 7 hrs 18 mins
d) 1 hr 12 mins
Q6 a) 2.33 hrs
b) 3.1 hrs
c) 0.33 hrs
Q7 a) Train 3
b) Train 1
c) 1208

Measures and Conversion Factors P.27

Q1 a) 200 cm   i) 6000 mm
b) 33 mm   j) 2000 kg
c) 4000 g   k) 3 kg
d) 0.6 kg   l) 86 mm
e) 0.65 km   m) 0.55 tonnes
f) 9000 g   n) 354 cm
g) 0.007 kg   o) 7 mm
h) 0.95 kg   p) 4.2 l
Q2 a) 0.47 m   b) 470 mm
Q3 a) 300 cm
b) 3000 mm
c) 0.003 km
Q4 a) 0.2 km
b) 2 km
c) 7 km
d) 0.02 km²
Q5 a) 167 cm
b) 33.3 cm
c) 333.3 cm²
d) 166.7 cm²
Q6 a) £4.69
b) £51.07

Scale Drawings P.28

Q1 10 cm long and 7.5 cm wide
Q2 65 cm long and 17 cm wide
Q3 13 mm wide gap, 78 cm wide oven.
Q4 a) Room 4 cm long and 3 cm wide
b) Window 2 cm, door 0.75 cm
Q5 a) 3.3 cm
b) 13.2 km
c) 48.8 km
Q6 a) 12.25 m
b) 4.02 m²

Answers: P.29 — P.41

Money P.29

Q1 The 12-egg box

Q2
a) 1.6 g
b) 2.5 g
c) The larger bar

Q3
a) 3.8 g
b) 3.9 g
c) The smaller tin

Q4
a) £181.82
b) £76.48
c) £956.32
d) £122.31
e) £1.67
f) £1120.69
g) £100.22
h) £16.53
i) £383.91
j) £377.81
k) £574.71
l) £0.83

Q5 Superstore — £9.03 per square yard

Interest P.30

Q1
a) £473.47
b) £612.52
c) £1065

Q2 Splitting the investment. £2.21 better.

Q3
a) £504
b) £1232
c) £16
d) £110 472.80

Q4
a) 4% compound interest gives £1040
5% simple interest gives £1050
£5 a month gives £1060
So the £5 a month account pays more.
b) 4% compound interest gives £4440.73
5% simple interest gives £4500
£5 a month gives £3600
So the 5% simple interest account pays more.
c) 4% compound interest gives £5864.84
5% simple interest gives £4950
£5 a month gives £3700
So the 4% compound interest account pays more.

Q5
a) £270
b) £790
c) £1130
d) £8012
e) £5100

Finance Questions P.31

Q1
a) £83.53
b) 18.4%
c) 6%

Q2
a) £125 000
b) £85 000
c) 47%

Q3
a) £5540
b) 16.2%
c) £8000

Q4
a) £12 000
b) £220
c) i) £35 ii) £20
d) £1050
e) £63.21
f) £9825

Rounding Numbers P.32-P.33

Q1
a) 62.2
b) 62.19
c) 62.194
d) 19.62433
e) 6.300
f) 3.141

Q2
a) 1330
b) 1330
c) 1329.6
d) 100
e) 0.02
f) 0.02469

Q3
a) 457.0
b) 456.99
c) 456.987
d) 457
e) 460
f) 500

Q4 2.83

Q5
a) 0.7
b) 3.25

Q6 23 kg

Q7 £5.07

Q8 235 miles

Q9 £19

Q10 £4.77

Q11 235 cm

Q12 4.5 m to 5.5 m

Q13
a) 142.465 kg
b) 142.455 kg

Q14
a) 32 cm ± 0.4 cm
b) ± (2x + 2y)

Accuracy and Estimating P.34-P.36

Q1
a) 807.87 m²
b) 808 m²
c) Part b) is more reasonable.

Q2
a) 3 s.f.
b) 2 s.f.
c) 3 s.f.
d) 2 s.f.
e) 1 s.f.
f) 2 s.f.

Q3
a) 43 g
b) 7.2 m
c) 3.429 g
d) 1.1 litres
e) 0.54 miles
f) 28.3 mpg

Q4
a) 14000
b) 12000
c) 300
d) 4.5
e) 5
f) 110
g) 14000
h) 500
i) 8000
j) 100
k) 60
l) 1

Q5 Approximately 15 000 – (1500 + 2500 + 1500 + 1500 + 3000) = 5000

Q6 150

Q7
a) 28
b) 522.6 tins/day
c) 14634 ≈ 15000 tins, 28 ≈ 30 days.
15000/30 = 500 tins/day

Q8
a) 3.0000000, 3.1428571, 3.1622777, 3.1481481, 3.1416667
b) $3\frac{17}{120}$

Q9
a) 2
b) 10
c) 100
d) 0.5

Q10
a) 1200 cm²
b) 20 km²

Q11
a) 39 m²
b) 3

Q12
a) 3 × 5² × 20 = 1500 cm³
b) 3 × 2² × 9 = 108 cm³

Q13 4500 cm³ — not big enough.

Q14
a) 20.1
b) 16.4
c) 15.8
d) 19.4
e) 19.8

Q15
a) 6.9
b) 10.9
c) 9.2
d) 4.1
e) 9.9
f) 5.8

Q16
a) 6.4
b) 14.1
c) 5.5
d) 12.2
e) 13.4
f) 11.8

Upper and Lower Bounds P.37-P.38

Q1
a) 64.785 kg
b) 64.775 kg

Q2 13.85 kg

Q3
a) 95 g
b) Upper: 97.5 g, lower: 92.5 g
c) No.

Q4
a) 1.75 m
b) 1.39 m²

Q5
a) Upper: 945, lower: 935
b) Upper: 5.565, lower: 5.555
c) Upper: 170.1, lower: 168.0
d) 170

Q6
a) Upper: 13.5, lower: 12.5
b) Upper: 12.55, lower: 12.45
c) Upper: 169.4, lower: 155.6

Q7 At least 18.2 m²

Q8 9.8 m/s

Q9 72.9 km/h

Q10
a) Upper: 5 mins 32.5 s, lower: 5 mins 27.5 s
b) Lower bound of Jimmy's time is 5 mins 25 s, which is faster than Douglas' lower bound, 5 mins 25.5 s.

Section Three

Conversion Graphs and Gradients P.39

Q1
a) £5
b) £9.50
c) £17
d) No

Q2
a) i) 12.5 miles ii) 44 miles iii) 56 miles
b) i) 64 km ii) 16 km iii) 48 km

Q3
a) kilometres/minute (speed)
b) kilograms/litre (density)
c) camels/km² (population density)

D/T and S/T Graphs P.40-P.42

Q1
a) 4 km
b) 15 mins and 45 mins
c) 2.4 km/h
d) 1100
e) 10 km/h
f) 1030

Q2
a) 1 hr 25 mins
b) 1 hr 20 mins
c) 25.4 km/h
d) 86.4 km/h
e) No. Can't get to Ingleton and back.

Q3

He waited 5 mins for the train.

Q4
a) A: 80 km/h B: 57 km/h C: 67 km/h
D: 44 km/h E: 50 km/h.
A was the fastest.
b) By the gradient. Steepest is fastest.

Q5 **a)** B
b) 3 mins 45 s
c) B
d) i) 267 m/min   **ii)** 16 km/h
e) C, 700 m/min or 42 km/h

Q6 **a)**
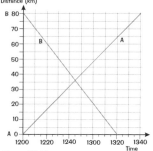

b) About 1245
c) About 36 km

Q7 **a)**
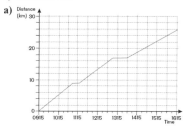

b) 25.75 km
c) 3.7 km/h
d) 5.14 km/h

Q8 **a)** 100 km/h
b) 2 hours
c) 100 km/h/h

Q9 **a) i)** 17.5 km   **ii)** 50 km
b) 102.5 km

Q10 105 m

Q11 140 m

Coordinates P.43

Q1
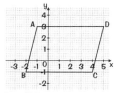

D = (5,3)

Q2
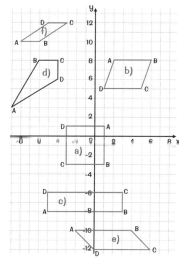

a) B is (1, -3)
b) C is (5, 5)
c) A is (-5, -8)
d) D is (-4, 6)
e) D is (0, -12)
f) C is (-3, 12)

Q3

C = (2, 1), D = (2, -2)

Midpoints of Line Segments P.44

Q1 **a)** (3,4)   **e)** (3,3.5)
b) (5.5,5)   **f)** (9.5,9.5)
c) (5.5,11)   **g)** (20,41.5)
d) (8.5,9)   **h)** (30.5,20.5)

Q2 (110, 135)

Q3 **a)** (2,5.5)   **e)** (2,3)
b) (0.5,1.5)   **f)** (4,–0.5)
c) (2,–2.5)   **g)** (–13,–12.5)
d) (1,–1)   **h)** (–5,–7)

Q4 **a)** (4,11)   **e)** (1,7)
b) (6.5,7.5)   **f)** (8.5,8)
c) (5.5,4)   **g)** (8.5,6.5)
d) (4.5,5)   **h)** (8.5,6)

Lengths of Line Segments P.45

Q1 AB: 5 (don't need Pythagoras)
CD: $\sqrt{10} = 3.16$
EF: $\sqrt{13} = 3.61$
GH: $\sqrt{8} = 2.83$
JK: $\sqrt{5} = 2.24$
LM: $\sqrt{26} = 5.10$
PQ: $\sqrt{20} = 4.47$
RS: $\sqrt{45} = 6.71$
TU: $\sqrt{13} = 3.61$

Q2 **a)** 5
b) $\sqrt{17} = 4.12$
c) 5
d) $\sqrt{58} = 7.62$
e) $\sqrt{26} = 5.10$
f) parallelogram

Q3 **a)** $\sqrt{41} = 6.40$
b) $\sqrt{98} = 9.90$
c) $\sqrt{53} = 7.28$
d) $\sqrt{34} = 5.83$
e) 4 (don't need Pythagoras here)
f) $\sqrt{37} = 6.08$

Q4 **a)** $\sqrt{10} = 3.16$
b) $\sqrt{130} = 11.40$
c) $\sqrt{8} = 2.83$
d) $\sqrt{233} = 15.26$
e) $\sqrt{353} = 18.79$
f) $\sqrt{100} = 10$

Q5 $x = 6$ or -2

Straight Line Graphs P.46-P.47

Q1 **a)** B   **f)** F
b) A   **g)** C
c) F   **h)** B
d) G   **i)** D
e) E   **j)** H

Q2

x	-4	-3	-2	-1	0	1	2	3	4
3x	-12	-9	-6	-3	0	3	6	9	12
y=3x-1	-13	-10	-7	-4	-1	2	5	8	11

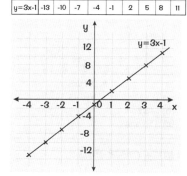

Q3

x	-6	-4	-2	0	2	4	6
½ x	-3	-2	-1	0	1	2	3
y=½x-3	-6	-5	-4	-3	-2	-1	0

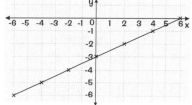

Q4

X	0	3	8
Y	3	9	19

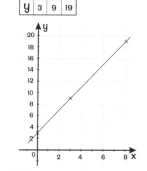

a) 13   **c)** 4
b) 7   **d)** 7

Q5

X	-8	-4	8
Y	-5	-4	-1

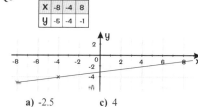

a) -2.5   **c)** 4
b) -3   **d)** 6

Answers: P.48 — P.54

Q6

Number of Units used	0	100	200	300
Cost using method A	10	35	60	85
Cost using method B	40	45	50	55

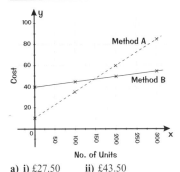

a) i) £27.50   ii) £43.50
b) Method A
c) 150 units

y = mx + c P.48-P.49

Q1
a) $m = 4, (0, 3)$ 　　l) $m = -\frac{5}{2}, (0, -2)$

b) $m = 3, (0, -2)$ 　　m) $m = \frac{1}{2}, (0, -\frac{3}{2})$

c) $m = 2, (0, 1)$ 　　n) $m = \frac{7}{3}, (0, \frac{5}{3})$

d) $m = -3, (0, 3)$ 　　o) $m = -1, (0, 0)$

e) $m = 5, (0, 0)$ 　　p) $m = 1, (0, 0)$

f) $m = -2, (0, 3)$ 　　q) $m = 1, (0, 3)$

g) $m = -6, (0, -4)$ 　　r) $m = 1, (0, -3)$

h) $m = 1, (0, 0)$ 　　s) $m = 3, (0, 7)$

i) $m = -\frac{1}{2}, (0, 3)$ 　　t) $m = 5, (0, 3)$

j) $m = \frac{1}{4}, (0, 2)$ 　　u) $m = -2, (0, -3)$

k) $m = \frac{4}{3}, (0, 2)$ 　　v) $m = 2, (0, 4)$

Q2
a) $-\frac{1}{2}$ 　　g) 4

b) 3 　　h) 1

c) $-\frac{1}{4}$ 　　i) -1

d) -2 　　j) $\frac{1}{3}$

e) $-\frac{2}{3}$ 　　k) $-\frac{1}{2}$

f) $-\frac{8}{3}$ 　　l) 3

Q3
a) $y = x + 4$ 　　d) $y = -x$
b) $y = 3x + 2$ 　　e) $y = -3x + 4$
c) $y = 2x + 9$ 　　f) $y = -2x - 3$

Q4
a) $y = \frac{7}{2}x - 1$ 　　d) $y = \frac{1}{4}x - 3$

b) $y = \frac{1}{2}x + 4$ 　　e) $y = -\frac{1}{2}x$

c) $y = -\frac{1}{5}x + 7$ 　　f) $y = -2x - 6$

Q5
a) $x = 4$ 　　c) $y = 7$
b) $x = 8$ 　　d) $y = 9$

Q6 $(7, 20)$ and $(5, 14)$

Q7
a) 2 　　d) -2

b) $\frac{1}{2}$ 　　e) $\frac{1}{2}$

c) -1 　　f) $-\frac{3}{4}$

Q8 The gradient is -0.23 so it's a red run.

Q9
a) $y = x$ 　　d) $y = -3x + 3$
b) $y = 3x$ 　　e) $y = -2x - 4$
c) $y = 2x + 1$ 　　f) $y = 5x + 3$

Equations from Graphs P.50-P.51

Q1

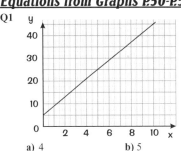

a) 4 　　b) 5
c) $y = 4x + 5$ 　　d) i) 29　ii) 45

Q2

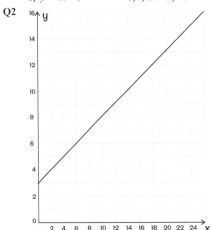

a) $\frac{1}{2}$ 　b) 3 　c) $y = \frac{1}{2}x + 3$

Q3 a) and d)

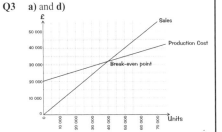

b) Design cost is £20 000.
   Manufacturing cost per unit is 30p.
c) $P = 0.3u + 20\,000$ (P = production cost, u = number of units)
e) Break-even point is 40 000 units.

Q4

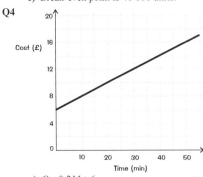

a) $C = 0.2M + 6$
b) £6
c) £12
d) i) £22 　ii) £26 　iii) £42

Q5

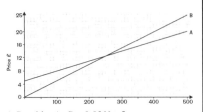

a) Provider A: $P = 0.03N + 5$
   Provider B: $P = 0.05N$
b) i) Provider A: £17; Provider B: £20
   ii) Provider A: £26; Provider B: £35
c) 250 units

Graphs to Recognise P.52-P.53

Q1
a) Reciprocal 　　f) Reciprocal
b) Reciprocal 　　g) Straight line
c) Reciprocal 　　h) Cubic
d) Quadratic 　　i) Cubic
e) Quadratic 　　j) Cubic

Q2
a) ix 　　g) viii
b) iv 　　h) vi
c) iii 　　i) x
d) vii 　　j) v
e) xi 　　k) ii
f) xii 　　l) i

Quadratic Graphs P.54

Q1

x	-4	-3	-2	-1	0	1	2	3	4
y=2x²	32	18	8	2	0	2	8	18	32

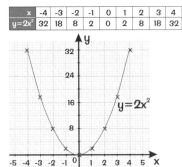

Q2

x	-4	-3	-2	-1	0	1	2	3	4
x²	16	9	4	1	0	1	4	9	16
y=x²+x	12	6	2	0	0	2	6	12	20

Answers: P.55 — P.57

Q3   a)

x	-4	-3	-2	-1	0	1	2	3	4
$-x^2$	-16	-9	-4	-1	0	-1	-4	-9	-16
$y = 3 - x^2$	-13	-6	-1	2	3	2	-1	-6	-13

b)

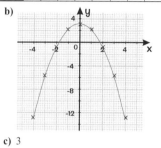

c) 3

Cubic Graphs P.55

Q1

x	-3	-2	-1	0	1	2	3
$y=x^3$	-27	-8	-1	0	1	8	27

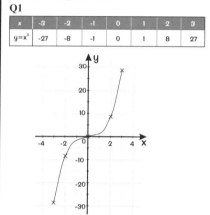

Q2

x	-3	-2	-1	0	1	2	3
$y=-x^3$	27	8	1	0	-1	-8	-27

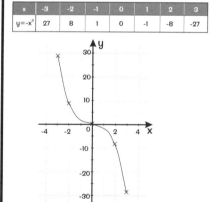

Q3

x	-3	-2	-1	0	1	2	3
x^3	-27	-8	-1	0	1	8	27
$y = x^3 + 4$	-23	-4	3	4	5	12	31

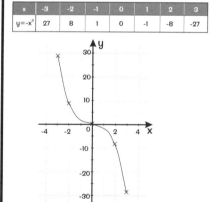

Q4

x	-3	-2	-1	0	1	2	3
$-x^3$	27	8	1	0	-1	-8	-27
$y = -x^3 - 4$	23	4	-3	-4	-5	-12	-31

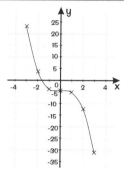

Q5   The graph has been moved 4 units up the y-axis.

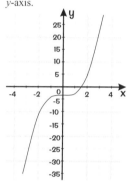

Q6   The graph has been moved 4 units down the y-axis.

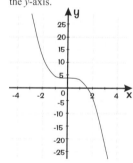

Graphs of Other Equations P.56

Q1

x	-4	-3	-2	-1	0	1	2	3	4
$y=1/x$	-0.25	-0.33	-0.5	-1	n/a	1	0.5	0.33	0.25

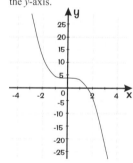

Q2

x	-4	-3	-2	-1	0	1	2	3	4
$1/x^2$	0.06	0.11	0.25	1	n/a	1	0.25	0.11	0.06
$y=3/x^2$	0.2	0.3	0.8	3	n/a	3	0.8	0.3	0.2

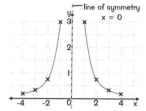

Q3   a)

x	-4	-3	-2	-1	0	1	2	3	4
$y=2^x$	0.06	0.1	0.3	0.5	1	2	4	8	16

b)

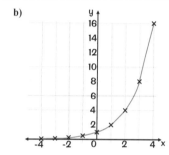

c) Anything to the power of 0 is 1.

Q4

x	-3	-2	-1	0	1	2	3
3^x	0.04	0.1	0.3	1	3	9	27
$6/x$	-2	-3	-6	n/a	6	3	2
$y=3^x - 6/x$	2.04	3.1	6.3	n/a	-3	6	25

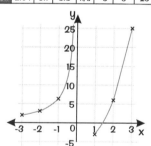

Section Four

Powers and Roots P.57-P.58

Q1
   a) 16
   b) 1000
   c) $3 \times 3 \times 3 \times 3 \times 3 = 243$
   d) $4 \times 4 \times 4 \times 4 \times 4 \times 4 = 4096$
   e) $1 \times 1 \times 1 \times 1 \times 1 \times 1 \times 1 \times 1 \times 1 = 1$
   f) $5 \times 5 \times 5 \times 5 \times 5 \times 5 = 15\ 625$

Q2
   a) 2^8 (or 256)   d) m^3
   b) 12^5 (or 248 832) e) y^4
   c) x^5 f) z^6

Q3
   b) 10^7
   c) 10^6
   d) 10^8
   e) Simply add the powers.

Q4
   b) 2^3
   c) 4^2
   d) 8^3
   e) Simply subtract the powers.

Answers: P.58 — P.64

Q5
a) true g) false
b) true h) true
c) false i) false
d) false j) true
e) true k) true
f) false l) false

Q6
a) 3^{-3} d) 3^{-12}
b) 4^{25} e) 4^6
c) 10^{-13} f) 5^3

Q7
a) 275 g) 10.4
b) 0.123 h) 0.843
c) 53 400 i) 2.25
d) 6.40×10^{-5} j) 2.18
e) 2.37 k) 0.244
f) 2.31 l) 0.965

Q8
a) 8.76 f) 91.9
b) 4.17 g) 13.6
c) 19.4 h) 17.8
d) 219 i) 5.06
e) 108

Q9
a) 0.008 g) 1.55
b) 0.25 h) 2.60
c) 1.53×10^{-5} i) 0.512
d) 0.667 j) 1.21
e) 2.24 k) 0.0352
f) 1.82 l) 7.28

Q10
a) 1.49 e) 1.08
b) 20.1 f) 8.78
c) 2.50 g) 0.707
d) 6.55 h) −0.380

Q11
a) 9.14 f) 1.22
b) 1.50 g) 84.5
c) 0.406 h) 0.496
d) 476 i) 165
e) 0.0146 j) 8.47

Sequences P.59-P.60

Q1
a) 9, 11, 13, add 2 each time
b) 32, 64, 128, multiply by 2 each time
c) 30000, 300000, 3000000, multiply by 10 each time
d) 19, 23, 27, add 4 each time
e) -6, -11, -16, take 5 off each time

Q2
a) 4, 7, 10, 13, 16
b) 3, 8, 13, 18, 23
c) 1, 4, 9, 16, 25
d) -2, 1, 6, 13, 22

Q3
a) $2n$ c) $5n$
b) $2n - 1$ d) $3n + 2$

Q4
a) 19, 22, 25, $3n + 4$
b) 32, 37, 42, $5n + 7$
c) 46, 56, 66, $10n - 4$
d) 82, 89, 96, $7n + 47$

Q5
a) $16\frac{7}{8}, 16\frac{9}{16}, 16\frac{23}{32}, 16\frac{41}{64}$
b) The 10th term will be the mean of the 8th and 9th.

Q6
a) The groups have 3, 8 and 15 triangles.
b) 24, 35, 48
c) $(n + 1)^2 - 1$

Q7
a) 23, 30, 38, $\frac{1}{2}(n^2 + 3n + 6)$
b) 30, 41, 54, $n^2 + 5$
c) 45, 64, 87, $2n^2 - 3n + 10$
d) 52, 69, 89, $\frac{1}{2}(3n^2 + n + 24)$
e) 9, 3, 1, 3^{7-n}
f) 50, 10, 2, $2 \times 5^{7-n}$

g) 48, 12, 3, $3 \times 4^{7-n}$
h) 63, 21, 7, $7 \times 3^{7-n}$

Q8
a) $\frac{(2n+1)^2 + 1}{2}$
b) $\frac{(2n+1)^2 - 1}{2}$
c) $(2n + 1)^2$

Basic Algebra P.61-P.63

Q1
a) -27°C d) +18°C
b) -22°C e) +15°C
c) +12°C f) -12°C

Q2 Expression **b)** is larger by 1.

Q3
a) $-4x$ b) $18y$

Q4
a) $-1000, -10$ c) 144, 16
b) $-96, -6$ d) 0, 0

Q5 -4

Q6
a) $-6xy$ g) $\frac{-5x}{y}$
b) $-16ab$ h) 3
c) $8x^2$ i) -4
d) $-16p^2$ j) -10
e) $\frac{10x}{y}$ k) $4x$
f) $\frac{-10x}{y}$ l) $-8y$

Q7
a) $15x^2 - x$
b) $13x^2 - 5x$
c) $-7x^2 + 12x + 12$
d) $30abc + 12ab + 4b$
e) $18pq + 8p$
f) $17ab - 17a + b$
g) $4pq - 5p - 9q$
h) $16x^2 - 4y^2$
i) $abc + 10ab - 11cd$
j) $-2x^2 + y^2 - z^2 + 6xy$

Q8
a) $4x + 4y - 4z$
b) $x^2 + 5x$
c) $-3x + 6$
d) $9a + 9b$
e) $-a + 4b$
f) $2x - 6$
g) $4e^2 - 2f^2 + 10ef$
h) $16m - 8n$
i) $6x^2 + 2x$
j) $-2ab + 11$
k) $-2x^2 - xz - 2yz$
l) $3x - 6y - 5$
m) $-3a - 4b$
n) $14pqr + 8pq + 35qr$
o) $x^3 + x^2$
p) $4x^3 + 8x^2 + 4x$
q) $8a^2b + 24ab + 8ab^2$
r) $7p^2q + 7pq^2 - 7q$
s) $16x - 8y$

Q9
a) $x^2 + 4x + 3x + 12 = x^2 + 7x + 12$
b) $4x^2 + 6x + 6x + 9 = 4x^2 + 12x + 9$
c) $15x^2 + 3x + 10x + 2 = 15x^2 + 13x + 2$

Q10
a) $(8x + 20)$ cm
b) $40x$ cm^2
c) $40x - 12x = 28x$ cm^2

Q11
a) $a^2(b + c)$ d) $a^2(a + y)$
b) $a^2(5 + 13b)$ e) $a^2(2x + 3y + 4z)$
c) $a^2(2b + 3c)$ f) $a^2(b^2 + ac^2)$

Q12
a) $4xyz(y + 2z)$
b) $4xyz(2xz + 3y)$
c) $8xyz(1 + 2x)$
d) $4xyz^2(5xy + 4)$

Q13
a) $x^2 - 2x - 3$
b) $x^2 + 2x - 15$
c) $x^2 + 13x + 30$
d) $x^2 - 7x + 10$
e) $x^2 - 5x - 14$
f) $28 - 11x + x^2$
g) $6x - 2 + 9x^2 - 3x = 9x^2 + 3x - 2$
h) $6x^2 - 12x + 4x - 8 = 6x^2 - 8x - 8$
i) $4x^2 + x - 12x - 3 = 4x^2 - 11x - 3$
j) $4x^2 - 8xy + 2xy - 4y^2$ $= 4x^2 - 4y^2 - 6xy$
k) $12x^2 - 8xy + 24xy - 16y^2$ $= 12x^2 - 16y^2 + 16xy$
l) $9x^2 + 4y^2 + 12xy$

Q14
a) $(4x + 6)$ m
b) $(-3x^2 + 17x - 10)$ m

Q15
a) $(x + 3)(x - 3)$
b) $(y + 4)(y - 4)$
c) $(5 + z)(5 - z)$
d) $(6 + a)(6 - a)$
e) $(2x + 3)(2x - 3)$
f) $(1 + 3xy)(1 - 3xy)$
g) $(5 + 4z)(5 - 4z)$
h) $(12 + y^2)(12 - y^2)$
i) $(x^2 + 6)(x^2 - 6)$
j) $(x^2 + y^2)(x^2 - y^2)$
k) $(7x^2y^2 + 1)(7x^2y^2 - 1)$
l) $(10x + 12y)(10x - 12y)$

Q16 $15x^2 + 4x - 4$

Q17 $4x^2 - 4x + 1$

Q18
a) Perimeter — $3x + 29$ cm
Area — $\frac{7x + 126}{2}$ cm^2
b) Perimeter — $(8x + 4)$ cm
Area — $(3x^2 + 14x - 24)$ cm^2
c) Perimeter — $(16x - 4)$ cm
Area — $(16x^2 - 8x + 1)$ cm^2
d) Perimeter — $(10x + 4)$ cm
Area — $(6x^2 - 5x - 6)$ cm^2

Q19
a) $(x + 3)(y + 1)$ b) $(x + 2)(2y + 5)$

Algebraic Fractions P.64-P.65

Q1
a) $\frac{3xy}{z}$ e) $3d$
b) $\frac{12b^2}{c}$ f) $\frac{4f^2}{g^3h}$
c) $\frac{1}{3xy^2z^3}$ g) $\frac{6j}{l^3}$
d) $\frac{q^3}{2r^3}$ h) $\frac{111}{1331}$

Q2
a) $\frac{2}{xy}$ g) $\frac{x^3}{5}$
b) $\frac{3a^2b}{2}$ h) $\frac{12a^3b^2}{5}$
c) $\frac{y}{2x^2}$ i) $\frac{3a^4c^3}{2b^2d}$
d) $\frac{2qr^2}{3}$ j) 1
e) $\frac{8x^3z^2}{y}$ k) $\frac{3t^2}{2}$
f) $\frac{90ac^4}{b}$ l) $\frac{d^6}{e^3f}$

Answers: *P.65 — P.70*

Q3 a) $2x^2y$ g) $\dfrac{12yz}{x}$

b) a h) $\dfrac{4a^3}{b}$

c) $\dfrac{3x^2}{y}$ i) $\dfrac{5a^3}{b}$

d) $\dfrac{pq}{2}$ j) $\dfrac{2x}{y^2z}$

e) $2ef$ k) $\dfrac{6}{n}$

f) $5x^3$ l) $\dfrac{7g}{f}$

Q4 a) $x = 5$ b) $x = 2$

Q5 a) $\dfrac{3+y}{2x}$ g) $\dfrac{3x+2+y}{24}$

b) $\dfrac{1+y}{x}$ h) $\dfrac{x+2y-2}{10}$

c) $\dfrac{2xy}{z}$ i) $\dfrac{7x}{6}$

d) $\dfrac{6x+1}{3}$ j) $\dfrac{37x}{42}$

e) $\dfrac{5x+6}{x}$ k) $\dfrac{x(y+3)}{3y}$

f) $\dfrac{14x+y}{6}$ l) $\dfrac{xyz+4x+4z}{4y}$

Q6 a) $\dfrac{4x-5y}{3}$ g) $\dfrac{z}{15}$

b) $\dfrac{4x-1}{y}$ h) $\dfrac{m(12-n)}{3n}$

c) $\dfrac{4x+3y-2}{2x}$ i) $\dfrac{b(14-a)}{7a}$

d) $\dfrac{2-2x}{x}$ j) $\dfrac{-p+5q}{10}$

e) $\dfrac{-1}{4x}$ k) $\dfrac{-3p-4q}{4}$

f) $\dfrac{4x-y}{6}$ l) $\dfrac{9x-4y+xy}{3y}$

Q7 a) $\dfrac{a^2}{b^2}$ f) $\dfrac{11}{6x}$

b) 1 g) $\dfrac{2(a^2+b^2)}{a^2-b^2}$

c) $\dfrac{3}{2r}$ h) $\dfrac{3}{4}$

d) $\dfrac{mn(pm+1)}{p^2}$ i) $\dfrac{3x-6y}{8}$

e) $\dfrac{2x}{x^2-y^2}$

Formulas from Words *P.66*

Q1 a) $y = x + 5$
b) $y = 7x + 4$
c) $y = (x - 7) \div 3$
d) $y = x + 6^2$ (or $y = x + 36$)
e) $y = x^2 \div 8$
f) $y = x^2 \div 12$

Q2 a) $c = 25n$
b) $c = (25 + 1.25)n = 26.5n$

Q3 a) $n + 23$
b) $n - 14$
c) $2n$
d) xn
e) nx^2

Q4 a) i) $4d$ cm ii) d^2 cm²
b) i) $a + b + c$ cm ii) $\frac{1}{2}cz$ cm²

Q5 $C = 10 + 5h$

Q6 $T = (73 + 27)p + 15l = 100p + 15l$

Q7 $S = (3 + \frac{1}{3}w)d$

Solving Equations *P.67-P.68*

Q1 1

Q2 a) $x = 5$ d) $x = -6$
b) $x = 4$ e) $x = 5$
c) $x = 10$ f) $x = 9$

Q3 a) $x = 5$ e) $x = 6$
b) $x = 2$ f) $x = 5$
c) $x = 8$ g) $x = 4$
d) $x = 17$

Q4 a) 15.5 cm b) 37.2 cm

Q5 £15.50

Q6 a) Joan — £x
Kate — £$2x$
Linda — £$(x - 232)$
b) $x + 2x + x - 232 = 2400$
$4x = 2632$
$x = 658$
c) Kate — £1316
Linda — £426

Q7 $x = 8$

Q8 $x = 1$

Q9 8 yrs

Q10 $x = 39$, so his wife is 35 and his son is 8.

Q11 a) $x = 9$ g) $x = 15$
b) $x = 2$ h) $x = 110$
c) $x = 3$ i) $x = \pm 6$
d) $x = 3$ j) $x = 66$
e) $x = 4$ k) $x = 700$
f) $x = -1$ l) $x = 7\frac{1}{2}$

Q12 a) $2x + 32$ cm
b) $12x$ cm²
c) $x = 3.2$

Q13 a) $x = \pm 3$ d) $x = \pm 3$
b) $x = \pm 6$ e) $x = \pm 1$
c) $x = \pm 3$ f) $x = \pm 3$

Q14 a) $x = 0.75$ d) $x = -1$
b) $x = -1$ e) $x = 4$
c) $x = -6$ f) $x = 13$

Q15 a) $y = 22$ f) $x = 7$
b) $x = 8$ g) $x = \pm 3$
c) $z = -5$ h) $x = \pm 4$
d) $x = 19$ i) $x = \pm 7$
e) $x = 23$

Q16 $x = 1\frac{1}{2}$

Q17 a) $x = 5$ b) $x = 9$

Q18 $x = 1\frac{1}{2}$ AB = 5 cm
AC = 5½ cm
BC = 7½ cm

Rearranging Formulas *P.69-P.70*

Q1 a) $h = \dfrac{10-g}{4}$ e) $g = \dfrac{8f}{3}$

b) $c = 2d - 4$ f) $x = 2(y + 3)$

c) $k = 3 + \dfrac{j}{2}$ g) $t = 6(s - 10)$

d) $b = \dfrac{3a}{2}$ h) $q = \dfrac{\sqrt{p}}{2}$

Q2 a) $c = \dfrac{w - 500m}{50}$ b) 132

Q3 a) i) £38.00 ii) £48.00
b) $c = 28 + 0.25n$
c) $n = 4(c - 28)$
d) i) 24 km ii) 88 km iii) 114 km

Q4 a) i) £2.04 ii) £3.48
b) $C = (12x + 60)$ pence

c) $x = \dfrac{C - 60}{12}$

d) i) 36 ii) 48 iii) 96

Q5 a) £Jx c) $J = \dfrac{T - P}{x}$
b) $P = T - Jx$ d) £16

Q6 a) $x = \sqrt{y + 2}$
b) $x = y^2 - 3$
c) $s = 2\sqrt{r}$
d) $g = 3f - 10$
e) $z = 5 - 2w$
f) $x = \sqrt{\dfrac{3v}{h}}$
g) $a = \dfrac{v^2 - u^2}{2s}$
h) $u = \sqrt{v^2 - 2as}$
i) $g = \dfrac{4\pi^2 l}{t^2}$

Q7 a) $x = \dfrac{z}{y + 2}$
b) $x = \dfrac{b}{a - 3}$
c) $x = \dfrac{y}{4 - z}$
d) $x = \dfrac{3z + y}{y + 5}$
e) $x = \dfrac{-2}{y - z}$ or $\dfrac{2}{z - y}$
f) $x = \dfrac{2y + 3z}{2 - z}$
g) $x = \dfrac{-y - wz}{yz - 1}$ or $\dfrac{y + wz}{1 - yz}$
h) $x = \dfrac{-z}{4}$

Q8 a) $p = \dfrac{4r - 2q}{q - 3}$
b) $g = \dfrac{5 - 2e}{f + 2}$
c) $b = \dfrac{3c + 2a}{a - c}$
d) $q = \pm\sqrt{\dfrac{4}{p - r}} = \pm\dfrac{2}{\sqrt{p - r}}$
e) $a = \dfrac{2c + 4b}{4 + c - d}$
f) $x = \pm\sqrt{\dfrac{-3y}{2}}$
g) $k = \pm\sqrt{\dfrac{14}{h - 1}}$
h) $x = \left(\dfrac{4 - y}{2 - z}\right)^2$
i) $a = \dfrac{b^2}{3 + b}$
j) $m = -7n$
k) $e = \dfrac{d}{50}$
l) $y = \dfrac{x}{3x + 2}$

Answers: P.71 — P.77

Q9

a) $y = \dfrac{x}{x-1}$

b) $y = \dfrac{-3-2x}{x-1}$ or $\dfrac{2x+3}{1-x}$

c) $y = \pm\sqrt{\dfrac{x+1}{2x-1}}$

d) $y = \pm\sqrt{\dfrac{1+2x}{3x-2}}$

Simultaneous Equations P.71

Q1
a) $x = 1, y = 2$
b) $x = 0, y = 3$
c) $x = -1\frac{1}{2}, y = 4$
d) $x = 1, y = 9$
e) $x = 8, y = -\frac{1}{2}$
f) $x = -1, y = 3$

Q2
a) $6x + 5y = 430$
$4x + 10y = 500$
b) $x = 45, y = 32$

Q3
a) $x = 3, y = 3$ f) $x = 1, y = 2$
b) $x = 2, y = 5$ g) $x = 2, y = 3$
c) $x = 1, y = 2$ h) $x = 2, y = 3$
d) $x = 1, y = 2$ i) $x = 5, y = 2$
e) $x = 1, y = 4$

Q4 5 g (jellies are 4 g)

Q5
a) $3y + 2x = 18$
$y + 3x = 6$ 　 $x = 0, y = 6$

b) $4y + 5x = 7$
$2x - 3y = 12$ 　 $x = 3, y = -2$

c) $4x - 6y = 13$
$x + y = 2$ 　 $x = 2\frac{1}{2}, y = -\frac{1}{2}$

Q6 $5m + 2c = 344$
$4m + 3c = 397$

$m = 34\text{p}, c = 87\text{p}$

Q7 $x = 12, y = 2$

Direct and Inverse Proportion P.72-P.73

Q1 $y = 20$

Q2 $y = 1.8$

Q3 a)

x	2	4	6
y	5	10	15

b)

x	3	6	9
y	4.5	9	13.5

c)

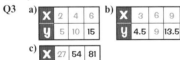

x	27	54	81
y	5	10	15

Q4 $y = 2$

Q5
a) $x = 4$
b) $y = 6$

Q6
a) 445 cm
b) 40

Q7
a) 4.5 m
b) 13.2 m
c) 0.9 m

Q8 $y = 184.8$

Q9 $x = 75$

Q10 $x = 2$

Q11

x	1	2	3	4	5	6
y	48	24	16	12	9.6	8

Q12 $y = 36$

Q13
a) $k = 1.6$
b) $y = 819.2$
c) $x = 11.5$

Q14

x	1	2	5	10
y	100	25	4	1

x	2	4	6	8
y	24	6	$2\frac{2}{3}$	1.5

Q15 4 kg

Q16
a) $r = 96$
b) $s = 4$
c) $r = 600$
d) $s = -8$

Q17 9.5 N kg⁻¹

Q18 $y \propto \dfrac{1}{x}$

a) $y = \dfrac{200}{x}$

b) $y = 31.25$

c) $x = 12.5$

Quadratics P.74-P.76

Q1
a) $(x+5)(x-2)$ 　 $x = -5, x = 2$
b) $(x-3)(x-2)$ 　 $x = 3, x = 2$
c) $(x-1)^2$ 　 $x = 1$
d) $(x-3)(x-1)$ 　 $x = 3, x = 1$
e) $(x-5)(x+4)$ 　 $x = 5, x = -4$
f) $(x+1)(x-5)$ 　 $x = -1, x = 5$
g) $(x+7)(x-1)$ 　 $x = -7, x = 1$
h) $(x+7)^2$ 　 $x = -7$
i) $(x-5)(x+3)$ 　 $x = 5, x = -3$

Q2
a) $(x+8)(x-2)$ 　 $x = -8, x = 2$
b) $(x+9)(x-4)$ 　 $x = -9, x = 4$
c) $(x+9)(x-5)$ 　 $x = -9, x = 5$
d) $x(x-5)$ 　 $x = 0, x = 5$
e) $x(x-11)$ 　 $x = 0, x = 11$
f) $(x-7)(x+3)$ 　 $x = 7, x = -3$
g) $(x-30)(x+10)$ 　 $x = 30, x = -10$
h) $(x-24)(x-2)$ 　 $x = 24, x = 2$
i) $(x-9)(x-4)$ 　 $x = 9, x = 4$
j) $(x+7)(x-2)$ 　 $x = -7, x = 2$
k) $(x+7)(x-3)$ 　 $x = -7, x = 3$
l) $(x-5)(x+2)$ 　 $x = 5, x = -2$
m) $(x-6)(x+3)$ 　 $x = 6, x = -3$
n) $(x-9)(x+7)$ 　 $x = 9, x = -7$
o) $(x+4)(x-3)$ 　 $x = -4, x = 3$

Q3 $x = \frac{1}{2}, x = -\frac{1}{2}$

Q4 $x = 4$

Q5
a) $(x^2 - x)\,\text{m}^2$　b) $x = 3$

Q6
a) $x(x+1)\,\text{cm}^2$　b) $x = 3$

Q7
a) $x^2\,\text{m}^2$　b) $12x\,\text{m}^2$
c) $x^2 + 12x - 64 = 0$ 　 $x = 4$

Q8
a) $x = 1.87, 0.13$　e) $x = 0.53, -4.53$
b) $x = 2.39, 0.28$　f) $x = -11.92, -15.08$
c) $x = 1.60, -3.60$　g) $x = -2.05, -4.62$
d) $x = 1.16, -3.16$　h) $x = 0.84, 0.03$

Q9
a) $x = -2, -6$　j) $x = 4, -5$
b) $x = 0.67, -0.5$　k) $x = 1, -3$
c) $x = 3, -2$　l) $x = 5, -1.33$
d) $x = 2, 1$　m) $x = 1.5, -1$
e) $x = 3, 0.75$　n) $x = -2.5, 1$
f) $x = 3, 0$　o) $x = 0.5, 0.33$
g) $x = 0.67$　p) $x = 1, -3$
h) $x = 0, -2.67$　q) $x = 2, -6$
i) $x = 4, -0.5$　r) $x = 2, -4$

Q10
a) $x = 0.30, -3.30$　h) $x = -0.59, -3.41$
b) $x = 3.65, -1.65$　i) $x = 7.12, -1.12$
c) $x = 0.62, -1.62$　j) $x = 13.16, 0.84$
d) $x = -0.55, -5.45$　k) $x = 1.19, -4.19$
e) $x = -0.44, -4.56$　l) $x = 1.61, 0.53$
f) $x = 1.62, -0.62$　m) $x = 0.44, -3.44$
g) $x = 0.67, -4.00$　n) $x = 2.78, 0.72$

Q11
a) $x = 1.7, -4.7$　g) $x = 1.12, -1.79$
b) $x = -0.27, -3.73$　h) $x = -0.21, -4.79$
c) $x = 1.88, -0.88$　i) $x = 2.69, -0.19$
d) $x = 0.12, -4.12$　j) $x = 2.78, 0.72$
e) $x = 4.83, -0.83$　k) $x = 1, 0$
f) $x = 1.62, -0.62$　l) $x = 1.5, 0.50$

Q12 $x^2 - 3.6x + 3.24 = 0$
$x = 1.8$

Q13
a) $x^2 + 2.5x - 144.29 = 0$
$x = 10.83$
b) 48.3 cm

Q14
a) $(x-2)^2 - 9$　g) $(x+1\frac{1}{2})^2 - 6\frac{1}{4}$
b) $(x-1)^2$　h) $(x-\frac{1}{2})^2 - 3\frac{1}{4}$
c) $(x+\frac{1}{2})^2 + \frac{3}{4}$　i) $(x-5)^2$
d) $(x-3)^2$　j) $(x-5)^2 - 25$
e) $(x-3)^2 - 2$　k) $(x+4)^2 + 1$
f) $(x-2)^2 - 4$　l) $(x-6)^2 - 1$

Q15
a) $x = 0.30, x = -3.30$
b) $x = 2.30, x = -1.30$
c) $x = 0.65, x = -4.65$
d) $x = 0.62, x = -1.62$
e) $x = 4.19, x = -1.19$
f) $x = 2.82, x = 0.18$
g) $x = 1.46, x = -0.46$
h) $x = 2.15, x = -0.15$

Functions P.77

Q1
a) $f(x) = 3 + x$
b) $f(x) = 790 - 41x$
c) $f(x) = 3(9x^2 + 2)$

Q2
a) $x = 4.5$　d) $x = \pm 2$
b) $x = \pm 1$　e) $x = 0.27$ or -7.27
c) $x = \pm 0.31$　f) $x = 5$

Q3
a) $f(5) = 9$　d) $f(5) = 13$
b) $f(5) = 30$　e) $f(5) = 2.2$
c) $f(5) = 38$　f) $f(5) = 520$

Q4
a) $f(8) = 44$
b) $g(3) = -6$
c) $f(-4) = -4$
d) $gf(x) = 3 - (4x + 12)^2$
e) $fg(x) = 4(3 - x^2) + 12$
f) $gf(2) = -397$

Q5
a) $f(-1) = 8$
b) $g(1/3) = 27$
c) $fh(x) = 6 - 2(6 + x^2)$
d) $gf(x) = 9 \div (6 - 2x)$
e) $fg(12) = 4.5$
f) $hf(-9) = 582$

Q6
a) $h^{-1}(x) = x - 6$

b) $f^{-1}(x) = \dfrac{11}{x} - 1$

c) $g^{-1}(h(x)) = \dfrac{4}{3}(6 + x)$

d) $f^{-1}(g(x)) = \dfrac{44}{3x} - 1$

e) $h^{-1}(f(5)) = -4.1\dot{6}$
f) $h^{-1}(g(-1)) = -6.75$

Q7
a) f(-1) = -0.67
b) g(9) = 5090
c) kj(-3) = 210
d) n⁻¹(2) = 14.5
e) 12
f) -0.75

Q8
a) $hi(x) = (22 \div (x^2 - x)) - 8$
b) $m^{-1}(x) = \frac{10(x-3)+12}{18} = \frac{10x-18}{18}$
c) $p^{-1}(q(x)) = \frac{(\frac{13}{x-2})-5}{8} = \frac{23-5x}{8x-16}$

Inequalities P.78-P.79

Q1
a) $9 \le x < 13$ **e)** $x > 25$
b) $-4 \le x < 1$ **f)** $-1 < x \le 3$
c) $x \ge -4$ **g)** $0 < x \le 5$
d) $x < 5$ **h)** $x < -2$

Q2
a)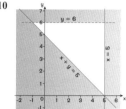
b)
c)
d)
e)
f)
g)
h)

Q3
a)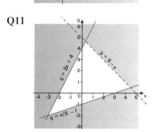
b)
c)
d)
e)
f)
g)
h)

Q4
a) $x > 3$ **i)** $x \ge 3$
b) $x < 4$ **j)** $x > 11$
c) $x \le 5$ **k)** $x < 3$
d) $x \le 6$ **l)** $x \ge -\frac{1}{2}$
e) $x \ge 7.5$ **m)** $x \le -2$
f) $x < 4$ **n)** $x > 5$
g) $x < 7$ **o)** $x < 15$
h) $x < 4$ **p)** $x \ge -2$

Q5 Largest integer for x is 2.

Q6 $\frac{11-x}{2} < 5$, $x > 1$

Q7 $1130 \le 32x$
$35.3125 \le x$
So 36 classrooms are needed.

Q8 Let number of guests = x
Then $900 \le 18x$
$50 \le x$
So the maximum is 50 guests (including bride and groom).

Q9 $x \ge 2$, $y > 1$, $x + y \le 5$

Q10
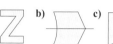

Q11
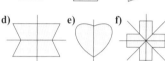

Using Graphical Inequalities P.80

Q1
a) $5B + 10C \le 100$
$C > B$
$B \ge 5$
b) & c)

d) B = 5, C = 6
B = 5, C = 7
B = 6, C = 7

Q2
a) $200A + 500B \le 10\,000$
$A + B \ge 40$
b) & c)

d) i) 35   **ii)** 6   **iii)** 206

Q3
a) $L \le 30$ $G > L$
$G + L \le 75$
b) $L \ge 0, G \ge 0$
c)
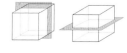
d) £421.50, 45 copies of G, 30 of L

Q4
a) T ≤ 12   T ≤ B
B ≤ 3T
b)
c) £91.20, 12 T and 36 B

Section Five
Symmetry P.81-P.82

Q1
a) **b)** **c)**
d) **e)** **f)**

Q2
a) 6   **c)** 5
b) 8   **d)** 3

Q3

M H V
1   2   1
Order of Rotation
1   1   2   2
A K S Z

Q4
a) Order of Rotation = 3
b) Order of Rotation = 1
c) Order of Rotation = 2
d) Order of Rotation = 1
e) Order of Rotation = 8
f) Order of Rotation = 2

Q5 E.g.

Answers: P.83 — P.87

Q6 No

Q7 Four. Three like this:

and one through its middle:

Q8 Infinitely many.

Q9 No

Q10 One of the following:

Q11 6

Q12 A point

Polygons P.83-P.84

Q1 Isosceles.

Q2

3cm

60° 60°

interior angle = 60°

Q3

order of rotational symmetry = 6.

Q4 **a)** ∠PQW = 90° + 60° = 150°

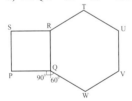

b) ∠PRW = 75°

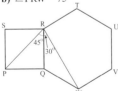

c) 180 – (360/n) = 150
180n – 360 = 150n
30n = 360 => n = 12

Q5 **a)** Interior angle = 165°
b) Exterior angle = 180° – 165° = 15°
Sum of exterior angles = 15 × 24 = 360°

Q6 **a)** $\frac{360}{5} = 72°$

b) $\frac{180 - 72}{2} = 54°$

c) i) 90° **ii)** 36°

d) Lines ST and BE are parallel, so angle ABE = angle BAS = 36° (alternate angles).
Triangle ABE is isosceles, so angle BEA = angle ABE = 36°.

Q7 (n – 2)180 = 2520
n = 16

Q8 **a)** $(\frac{360}{5}) \div 2 = 36°$

b) OX = 5 cos 36 = 4.045 cm
Hence MX = 5 – 4.045 = 0.95 cm

Q9 **a)**

b) Angle CDE = angle DEF
$= \frac{(8 - 2)180}{8} = 135$

so angle EFC = $\frac{360 - 2(135)}{2} = 45°$

or exterior angle = angle EFC = 45° (alternate angles).

Q10 **a)** Angles at a point sum to 360°, hence m + m + r = 360°.
Interior angles in a pentagon sum to 540°. We know two angles are 90°, so we are left with 540° – 180° = 360°. The only angles left are m, m and r so m + m + r must equal 360°.

b) r°

c)

Q11 540° – (100° + 104° + 120°)
= 216° for two equal angles
∴ 1 angle = 108°

Perimeters and Areas P.85-P.86

Q1 Area 24 cm², perimeter 20 cm

Q2 Area 25 cm², perimeter 20 cm

Q3 Area = 120 cm²

Q4 **a)** length = 24, width = 12, area = 288 m²
b) 1 Carpet tile = 0.50 × 0.50 = 0.25 m²
So 288 m² ÷ 0.25 = 1152 tiles are required.
c) £4.99 per m² => £4.99 for 4 tiles
Total cost = (1152 ÷ 4) × 4.99
= £1437.12

Q5 Each square = 0.6 m × 0.6 m = 0.36 m².
Total area of material = 6 × 0.36 = 2.16 m².

Q6 Perimeter = $4 \times \sqrt{9000}$
= 379.47 m (2 d.p.)
Natasha ran: 11 × 379.47
= 4200 m (to nearest 100 m)

Q7 48 ÷ 5 = 9.6 m length.
Area of 1 roll = 11 m × 0.5 m = 5.5 m².
48 m² ÷ 5.5 m² = $8\frac{8}{11}$ rolls of turf required.
So 9 should be ordered.

Q8 Base length = 4773 ÷ 43 = 111 mm.

Q9 Area of metal blade
= ½ × 35 × (70 + 155) = 3937.5 mm²

Q10 Area of larger triangle
= ½ × 14.4 × 10 = 72 cm².
Area of inner triangle
= ½ × 5.76 × 4 = 11.52 cm².
Area of metal used for a bracket
= 72 – 11.52 = 60.48 cm².
So it will not take the weight.

Q11 T₁: ½ × 8 × 16 = 64 m²
Tr₁: ½ × 8 × (8 + 16) = 96 m²
Tr₂: ½ × 4 × (8 + 12) = 40 m²
T₂: ½ × 8 × 12 = 48 m²
Total area of glass sculpture = 248 m²

Q12 **a)** Area = (4 × 4) – ((1 × 2) + (½ × π ×1²))
+ (½ × π × 2²)
= 16 – 3.5708 + 6.2832
= 18.7 m² (1 d.p.)

b) Three 1 litre tins of paint are needed for two coats.

c) Perimeter = 1 + 1 + (½ × π × 2)
+ 1 + 1 + 4 + (½ × π × 4) + 4
= 12 + 3π = 21.4 m (1 d.p.)

Q13 Area = ½ × 8.2 × 4.1 = 16.81 m²
To find third side:
$\sqrt{10.8^2 - 4.1^2} = 9.99$ m
9.99 – 8.2 = 1.79 m
Third side = $\sqrt{1.79^2 + 4.1^2}$
= 4.5 m (2 s.f.)
Perimeter = 10.8 + 4.5 + 8.2
= 23.5 m.

Q14 **a)** Area of each isosceles triangle
= ½ × 2.3 × 3.2 = 3.68 m²
b) Area of each side =
$(\sqrt{3.2^2 + 1.15^2}) \times 4 = 13.6$ m²
Groundsheet = 2.3 × 4 = 9.2 m²
c) Total material =
(2 × 3.68) + 9.2 + (2 × 13.6) = 43.8 m²

Q15

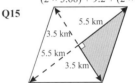

5.5 km
3.5 km
5.5 km
3.5 km

Area = 2(½ × 3.5 × 11)
= 2 × 19.25 = 38.5 km².

Solids and Nets P.87-P.88

Q1 E.g.

X   Base   X
F   Y

Q2

3 cm
2 cm   2 cm   3 cm
Base   4 cm

Other arrangements are possible.

Q3

Base
3 cm

Q4

Q5 a) Rectangle.

b) AH, CF, BG.

c) DF, AG, BH.

d) HC, BE, AF.

e) 8

Q6 a) 1 b) 1

Q7 a) 12 b) 7 c) 7

Q8 a) H, F and D

b) Line symmetry through lines AF, DH, BG and CE. Rotational symmetry of order 4.

c) 5 faces and vertices, 8 edges.

Q9 a) I

b) 64 cm²

c) 64 × 6 = 384 cm²

Q10 E.g.

Q11 Net B

Q12 a) E.g.

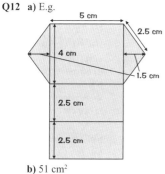

b) 51 cm²

Surface Area and Volume
P89-P91

Q1 a) $\frac{1}{2}\pi(0.35)^2 = 0.192$ m²

b) 0.1924 × 3 = 0.577 m³

Q2 a) $\pi(2.5^2 - 2^2) = 7.07$ m²

£16 × 7.07 = £113.12 = £110 to nearest £10.

b) Volume = $\pi(2)^2 \times 0.50 = 6.28$ m³

so use 6.28 × 15 = 94 ml treatment to the nearest ml.

Q3 a) Volume Cube = Volume Cylinder

$10^3 = \pi r^2 \times 10$ so $r^2 = \frac{10^2}{\pi}$,

$r = 5.64$ cm

b) S.A. of cylinder = $2\pi rh + 2\pi r^2 =$

$(2\pi \times 5.64...) \times (10 + 2\pi \times (5.64...)^2)$

= 554.49 cm².

Q4 a) $\pi(5)^2(16) = 1257$ cm³

b) $\pi(5)^2 h = 600$

$h = \frac{600}{25\pi} = 7.64$ cm

Q5 $(3)(3)(0.5) - \pi(0.7)^2(0.5) = 3.73$ cm³

Q6 $(\pi \times (2)^2 \times 110) +$

$(\frac{1}{2}(14 + 20) \times 6 \times 20) = 3422.30$ cm³

2 × 3422.30 = 6844.60 cm³ = 6.84 litres

Q7 a) (60)(30) + (30)(120) = 5400 cm²

b) 5400 × 100 = 540000 cm³ = 0.54 m³

Q8 $AB^2 = 2^2 + 1.5^2$ AB = 2.5 m

1 panel on roof = $\frac{1}{2}AB \times \frac{5}{2}$

= 1.25 × 2.5 = 3.125 m²

Front of greenhouse =

(2.5 × 4) + (½ × 4 × 1.5) = 13 m²

Total = 3.125 + 13 = 16.125 m²

Q9 a) $x(3 - x)(5 - x)$ m³ or $x^3 - 8x^2 + 15x$

b)

x	0	1	2	3
V	0	8	6	0

c)

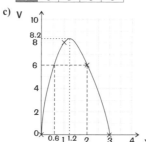

d) about 8.2 m³

e) ends: 2(1.2)(1.8) = 4.32 +

side faces: 2(1.2)(3.8) = 9.12 +

tops: 2(3.8)(1.8) = 13.68

So area is about 27.12 m²

f) x = 2 or x = 0.6

If x = 0.6 :

ends 2(0.6)(2.4) = 2.88 +

side faces 2(0.6)(4.4) = 5.28 +

tops 2(2.4)(4.4) = 21.12

  29.28 m²

If x = 2 :

ends 2(2)(1) = 4 +

side faces 2(2)(3) = 12 +

tops 2(1)(3) = 6

  22 m²

Maximum Total S.A. ≈ 29.28 m²

Q10 a) $\frac{1}{2}(\frac{4}{3}\pi(1.3)^3) + \pi(1.3)^2 \times 1.8$

$+ \frac{1}{3}\pi(1.3)^2 \times 1.2 = 16.28$ cm³

b) Volume of sand in hemisphere and cone parts remain the same so change is in cylindrical part.

Therefore h + 0.3 = 1.8,

h = 1.5 cm.

c) Volume of sand transferred =

$\frac{1}{2}(\frac{4}{3}\pi(1.3)^3) + \pi(1.3)^2 \times 1.5 = 12.57$ cm³

Time Taken = $\frac{12.57}{0.05} \approx 251$ secs.

= 4 minutes 11 secs.

Q11 a) Volume of ice cream

$= \frac{1}{3}\pi(2.5^2 \times 10) - \frac{1}{3}\pi(1^2 \times 4)$

$+ \frac{1}{2}(\frac{4}{3}\pi \times 2.5^3)$

= 93.99 cm³ of ice cream.

b) Outer surface area of cone = $\pi r l$

Using Pythagoras,

$l^2 = 10^2 + 2.5^2 = 106.25$,

l 10.3 cm.

So S.A. = $\pi \times 2.5 \times 10.3 = 81.0$ cm².

Q12 Vol. increase is a cylinder of height 4.5 cm.

So vol. increase = $\pi(5)^2 \times 4.5 = 353.4$ cm³.

Volume of each marble = $\frac{353.4}{200}$

= 1.767 cm³

$\frac{4}{3}\pi r^3 = 1.767 \Rightarrow r = 0.75$ cm

Q13 a) 4000 m³

b) 1665 m² c) 85 litres

Congruence, Similarity and Enlargements P92-P93

Q1 ABC and DEF are congruent — same size angles and side lengths.

Q2 a) Angle DAE shared. Parallel lines make corresponding angles equal so the triangles are similar.

b) Ratio of lengths given by $\frac{AB}{AD} = \frac{12}{20} = \frac{3}{5}$

So $x = 25 \times \frac{3}{5} = 15$ cm

Also $\frac{y + 10}{y} = \frac{5}{3}$

$\Rightarrow 2y = 30, y = 15$ cm

Q3

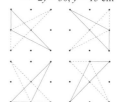

Hence 7 ways to draw another.

Q4 a) & b)

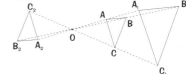

c) triangle $A_2B_2C_2$

Q5 Widths in ratio 2:3, so volumes in ratio 8:27.

Volume = $30 \times \frac{27}{8} = 101$ litres

Q6 a) All lengths must be enlarged in the same ratio for them to be similar.

b) 4 litres

Q7 a) Triangles APQ and STC (both isosceles and share either angle PAQ or SCT)

b) Ratio AC:AQ = 24:7.5 = 3.2:1

so AP = $15 \times \frac{1}{3.2} = 4.6875$ cm

PT = 24 – 2 (4.6875)

= 14.625 cm.

c) Using $\frac{1}{2}$(base)(height)

$= \frac{1}{2}(24)(9) = 108$ cm²

d) Scale factor = $\frac{1}{3.2}$

Area scale factor = $\frac{1}{10.24}$

Area of triangle APQ = $108 \times \frac{1}{10.24}$

= 10.5 cm²

e) 108 – 2 (10.5) = 87 cm²

Q8 a) 2 end faces 2 × (2 × 3) = 12 cm²

2 side faces 2 × (5 × 3)

= 30 cm²

Top & bottom 2 × (5 × 2)

= 20 cm²

Total = 62 cm²

b) SF for length = 1:4

SF for area = 1:16

new area = 62 × 16 = 992 cm²

Answers: P.94 — P.98

Q9 **a)** volume = $\frac{1}{3}\pi(100^2)(100)$
= 1047198 cm³
= 1.05 m³
b) 50 cm
c) ratio = 1:2³ = 1:8
d) Volume of small cone =
1.05 × $\frac{1}{8}$ = 0.131 m³
e) volume of portion left =
1.05 – 0.131 = 0.919
so ratio = 0.919:0.131 = $\frac{0.919}{0.131}$:1 = 7:1

Loci and Constructions P.94-P.95

Q1

Not to scale

Q2

Not to scale
Length BA = 0.9 cm

Q3
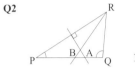
Not to scale

Q4
Not to scale
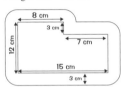
Radius of the circle = 2.7 cm

Q5 **a)** A circle with diameter AB.
b) and **c)**
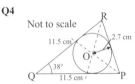
Not to scale

d) The ship comes 1.7 cm = 0.85 km from the rocks.

Q6
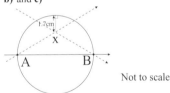
Not to scale

Q7 **a)**
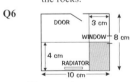

b) Distance around dashed path =
(2 × 100) + (π × 65) = 404.2 m

Q8
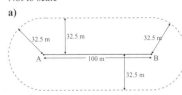
Not to scale

Q9 **a)**
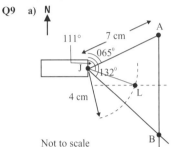
Not to scale

b) Length of AB
= 8.6 cm equivalent to 43 km.
c) 35 km in 2.5 hrs,
so speed = $\frac{35}{2.5}$ = 14 km/h.
d) see diagram
e) Bearing from L to J = 111°

Section Six
Vectors P.96-P.97

Q1 **a)**

b) i) $\begin{pmatrix} -1 \\ -4 \end{pmatrix}$
ii) $\begin{pmatrix} 4 \\ 0 \end{pmatrix}$
iii) $\begin{pmatrix} 5 \\ 4 \end{pmatrix}$
c) Isosceles

Q2 **a)** $\begin{pmatrix} 2 \\ 1 \end{pmatrix}$ $\underset{\sim}{p}+\underset{\sim}{q}$

b) $\begin{pmatrix} 2 \\ 5 \end{pmatrix}$ $\underset{\sim}{p}-\underset{\sim}{q}$

c) $\begin{pmatrix} 6 \\ -2 \end{pmatrix}$ $2\underset{\sim}{r}$

d) $\begin{pmatrix} 1 \\ 1 \end{pmatrix}$ $\underset{\sim}{s}+\underset{\sim}{p}$

e) $\begin{pmatrix} 6 \\ 10 \end{pmatrix}$

$2\underset{\sim}{p}-2\underset{\sim}{s}$

f) $\begin{pmatrix} -1 \\ -8 \end{pmatrix}$
$3\underset{\sim}{q}+\underset{\sim}{s}$

g) $\begin{pmatrix} 6 \\ 0 \end{pmatrix}$
$2\underset{\sim}{r}-\underset{\sim}{q}$

h) $\begin{pmatrix} 6 \\ -3 \end{pmatrix}$
$\frac{1}{2}\underset{\sim}{q}+2\underset{\sim}{r}$

i) $\begin{pmatrix} 0 \\ -1 \end{pmatrix}$ $\underset{\sim}{p}+2\underset{\sim}{s}$

j) $\begin{pmatrix} -6 \\ 0 \end{pmatrix}$
$\underset{\sim}{q}-2\underset{\sim}{r}$

Q3 **a)** $2\underset{\sim}{y}$ **d)** $2\underset{\sim}{y}+2\underset{\sim}{x}$
b) $\underset{\sim}{y}+\underset{\sim}{x}$ **e)** $4\underset{\sim}{y}+2\underset{\sim}{x}$
c) $\underset{\sim}{y}-\underset{\sim}{x}$ **f)** $2\underset{\sim}{x}$

Q4 **a) i)** $\overrightarrow{ED}$ or $\overrightarrow{AF}$ **v)** $\overrightarrow{BE}$
ii) $\overrightarrow{EF}$ or $\overrightarrow{DC}$ **vi)** $\overrightarrow{AC}$
iii) $\overrightarrow{AE}$ **vii)** $\overrightarrow{EC}$ or $\overrightarrow{AB}$
iv) $\overrightarrow{BA}$ **viii)** $\overrightarrow{EB}$
b) i) 48 cm²   **ii)** 60 cm²
c) i) 8.54 cm   **iv)** 16.3 cm
ii) 3 cm   **v)** 8.54 cm
iii) 8 cm   **vi)** 10 cm

Q5 9.5 km/h
Q6 **a)** 55°   **b)** 2.9 km/h
Q7 **a)** 353°   **b)** 595 km/h
Q8 **a) i)** $\begin{pmatrix} 5 \\ 14 \end{pmatrix}$ **ii)** $\begin{pmatrix} 5 \\ 4 \end{pmatrix}$
b) i) 3.6   **iii)** 6.1
ii) 10   **iv)** 11.4
Q9 **i) a)** 15.6 N
b) 40°
ii) a) 18.0 N
b) 34°
iii) a) 30.5 N
b) 41.0°

Matrices P.98-P.99

Q1 **a)** $\begin{pmatrix} 9 & 9 \\ 11 & 7 \end{pmatrix}$ **f)** $\begin{pmatrix} 31 & 31 \\ -10 & -38 \end{pmatrix}$
b) $\begin{pmatrix} 3 & 2 \\ -4 & 6 \end{pmatrix}$ **g)** $\begin{pmatrix} 9 & -1 & -1 \\ 9 & 13 & 1 \end{pmatrix}$
c) $\begin{pmatrix} 4 & 23 \\ 18 & 14 \end{pmatrix}$ **h)** $\begin{pmatrix} 2 & 8 & -14 \\ -5 & 11 & -2 \end{pmatrix}$
d) $\begin{pmatrix} -9 & 0 \\ 12 & 10 \end{pmatrix}$ **i)** $\begin{pmatrix} 7 & -9 \\ 6 & -2 \\ 2 & 2 \end{pmatrix}$
e) $\begin{pmatrix} -4 & 10 \\ 15 & 5 \end{pmatrix}$

Q2 **a)** No   **d)** Yes
b) Yes   **e)** Yes
c) No

Q3 **a)** $\begin{pmatrix} 6 & 15 \\ 3 & 21 \end{pmatrix}$ **e)** $\begin{pmatrix} 8 & 32 & -4 \\ 36 & 24 & -12 \end{pmatrix}$
b) $\begin{pmatrix} 32 & 80 \\ 40 & 48 \end{pmatrix}$ **f)** $\begin{pmatrix} -21 & -3 & -9 \\ 6 & -12 & 3 \end{pmatrix}$
c) $\begin{pmatrix} -8 & -3 \\ -13 & 5 \end{pmatrix}$ **g)** $\begin{pmatrix} 18 & -10 \\ -4 & -6 \\ 14 & -2 \end{pmatrix}$
d) $\begin{pmatrix} 10 & -25 \\ -55 & -15 \end{pmatrix}$ **h)** $\begin{pmatrix} -24 & 32 & -40 \\ -72 & 16 & -8 \end{pmatrix}$

Answers: *P.99 — P.105*

Q4 **a)** $\begin{pmatrix} 13 & 47 \\ 13 & 53 \end{pmatrix}$ **f)** $\begin{pmatrix} 51 \\ 73 \end{pmatrix}$

b) $\begin{pmatrix} 19 & -19 \\ 40 & -14 \end{pmatrix}$ **g)** $\begin{pmatrix} -15 & -6 & -12 & -24 & 3 \\ -5 & -2 & -4 & -8 & 1 \end{pmatrix}$

c) $\begin{pmatrix} 145 & -185 \\ 58 & -74 \end{pmatrix}$ **h)** $(-12 \ \ 19 \ \ 11)$

d) $\begin{pmatrix} 2 & 10 & 8 \\ 6 & 30 & 24 \\ -3 & -15 & -12 \end{pmatrix}$ **i)** $\begin{pmatrix} -11 & -13 \\ 73 & -5 \end{pmatrix}$

e) $\begin{pmatrix} 61 & 33 & 34 \\ 4 & 23 & 19 \end{pmatrix}$

Q5 **a)** $\begin{pmatrix} 1 & 7 \\ -1 & 17 \end{pmatrix}$ **e)** $\begin{pmatrix} 16 & 22 \\ -11 & 38 \end{pmatrix}$

b) $\begin{pmatrix} 5 & -2 \\ -7 & 0 \end{pmatrix}$ **f)** $\begin{pmatrix} 50 & 60 \\ -57 & -51 \end{pmatrix}$

c) $\begin{pmatrix} -20 & -40 \\ -15 & 20 \end{pmatrix}$ **g)** $\begin{pmatrix} -12 & -15 & 3 \\ -24 & -6 & -30 \end{pmatrix}$

d) $\begin{pmatrix} 22 & 55 \\ 121 & -11 \end{pmatrix}$ **h)** $\begin{pmatrix} -1 & 33 \\ 33 & 13 \end{pmatrix}$

Q6 **a)** $\begin{pmatrix} 0 & 0 \\ 0 & 0 \end{pmatrix}$ **c)** $\begin{pmatrix} 8 & 12 \\ 2 & 3 \end{pmatrix}$

b) $\begin{pmatrix} 4 & -15 \\ 7 & 100 \end{pmatrix}$ **d)** $\begin{pmatrix} 91 & -50 \\ -1 & 2 \end{pmatrix}$

Q7 $(3 \times 14) - (7 \times 6) = 42 - 42 = 0$
The determinant is zero, so the matrix is singular.

Q8 **a)** $\frac{1}{20}\begin{pmatrix} 3 & -1 \\ -4 & 8 \end{pmatrix}$ **e)** $ad - bc$ $= -36 - (-36) = 0$

b) $ad - bc$ $= 18 - 18 = 0$ **f)** $\frac{1}{12}\begin{pmatrix} 5 & -9 \\ 3 & -3 \end{pmatrix}$

c) $-\frac{1}{43}\begin{pmatrix} -2 & -7 \\ -5 & 4 \end{pmatrix}$ **g)** $\frac{1}{60}\begin{pmatrix} -3 & 5 \\ -6 & -10 \end{pmatrix}$

d) $ad - bc$ $= 8 - 8 = 0$ **h)** $\frac{1}{177}\begin{pmatrix} 11 & -5 \\ 9 & 12 \end{pmatrix}$

Q9 **a)** No. If $\underline{A} \times \underline{B} =$ the identity matrix, then $\underline{B} = \underline{A}^{-1}$ (the inverse of $\underline{A}$), and you can only find $\underline{A}^{-1}$ if $\underline{A}$ is not singular.
b) Yes. If $\underline{D}$ is a zero matrix, then $\underline{C} \times \underline{D} =$ a zero matrix.

Q10 **a)** $\begin{pmatrix} 9 & 7 \\ 15 & 5 \end{pmatrix}$ **g)** $\begin{pmatrix} 5 & -14 \\ 27 & 23 \end{pmatrix}$

b) $\begin{pmatrix} -13 & 9 \\ -9 & 3 \end{pmatrix}$ **h)** $\frac{1}{23}\begin{pmatrix} 1 & 1 \\ -12 & 11 \end{pmatrix}$

c) $\begin{pmatrix} -1 & 2 \\ -10 & -9 \end{pmatrix}$ **i)** $\begin{pmatrix} 1 & 0 \\ 0 & 1 \end{pmatrix}$

d) $\begin{pmatrix} 22 & -2 \\ 24 & 2 \end{pmatrix}$ **j)** $\begin{pmatrix} 11 & -1 \\ 12 & 1 \end{pmatrix}$

e) $\begin{pmatrix} -26 & 115 \\ -43 & 115 \end{pmatrix}$ **k)** $\begin{pmatrix} 0 & 0 \\ 0 & 0 \end{pmatrix}$

f) $\begin{pmatrix} 74 & 10 \\ 81 & 1 \end{pmatrix}$ **l)** $\begin{pmatrix} -2 & 8 \\ 3 & 4 \end{pmatrix}$

Transformations *P.100-P.103*

Q1 **a), b), c)** — see diagram.

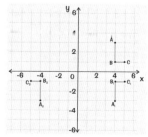

d) Rotation of 180° about (0, 0)

Q2 **a), b), d), e)** — see diagram

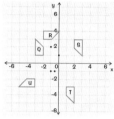

c) Rotation 180° about (0, 2).
f) 90° rotation anticlockwise about $\left(-\frac{1}{2}, -\frac{1}{2}\right)$.

Q3 **a)**

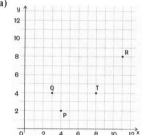

b) $\overrightarrow{QO} = \begin{pmatrix} -3 \\ -4 \end{pmatrix}$
$T = \begin{pmatrix} 11 \\ 8 \end{pmatrix} + \begin{pmatrix} -3 \\ -4 \end{pmatrix} = \begin{pmatrix} 8 \\ 4 \end{pmatrix}$
See diagram for point T.
c) $\begin{pmatrix} -1 \\ 2 \end{pmatrix} + \begin{pmatrix} 8 \\ 4 \end{pmatrix} + \begin{pmatrix} -3 \\ -4 \end{pmatrix} + \begin{pmatrix} -4 \\ -2 \end{pmatrix} = \begin{pmatrix} 0 \\ 0 \end{pmatrix} = O$

Q4 **a)** to **e)** — see diagram.

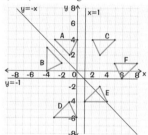

f) Rotation of 180°, centre (3, 0)

Q5 **a), b)** — see diagram.

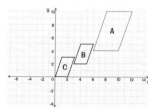

c) Ratio of areas C:A = 1:4

Q6 **a)** to **c)** — see diagram.

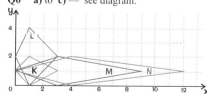

Q7 **a)** Shear with the *x*-axis invariant, with a shear factor of $\frac{4}{5}$.
b) Shear with the *y*-axis invariant, with a shear factor of $\frac{2}{3}$.

c)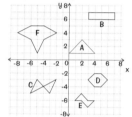

e)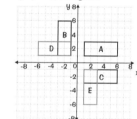

d)

Q8 **a)** 90° rotation anticlockwise, about (-2, 0).
b) Reflection in the *x*-axis, followed by a shear with invariant line $y = 2$ and shear factor 1.
c) Stretch of scale factor 4 with the *x*-axis invariant, followed by translation of $\begin{pmatrix} 1 \\ -1 \end{pmatrix}$.

Q9 **a)-f)** — see diagram

Q10 **a)-e)** — see diagram

Q11 **a)** $\begin{pmatrix} 1 & 3 & 4 & 2 \\ 5 & 5 & 7 & 7 \end{pmatrix}$ **f)** $\begin{pmatrix} 5 & 7 & 6 \\ -2 & -2 & -4 \end{pmatrix}$

b) $\begin{pmatrix} -5 & -5 & -7 & -7 \\ 1 & 3 & 4 & 2 \end{pmatrix}$ **g)** $\begin{pmatrix} 0 & 1 \\ -1 & 0 \end{pmatrix}$

c) $\begin{pmatrix} 2 & 4 & 2 \\ 1 & 1 & 4 \end{pmatrix}$ **h)** $\begin{pmatrix} -1 & 0 \\ 0 & -1 \end{pmatrix}$

d) $\begin{pmatrix} -2 & -4 & -2 \\ -1 & -1 & -4 \end{pmatrix}$ **i)** $\begin{pmatrix} 1 & 0 \\ 0 & -1 \end{pmatrix}$

e) $\begin{pmatrix} 5 & 7 & 6 \\ 2 & 2 & 4 \end{pmatrix}$

Q12 **a)** $\begin{pmatrix} 8 & 14 & 14 & 8 \\ 2 & 2 & 7 & 7 \end{pmatrix}$

b) $\begin{pmatrix} 6 & 16 & 8 \\ -3 & -1 & -5 \end{pmatrix}$ **c)** $\begin{pmatrix} -16 & -25 & 14 & 23 \\ -12 & -15 & -12 & -9 \end{pmatrix}$

Geometry *P.104-P.105*

Q1 **a)** $x = 47°$
b) $y = 154°$
c) $z = 22°$
d) $p = 35°$, $q = 45°$

Q2 **a)** $a = 146°$
b) $m = 131°$, $z = 48°$
c) $x = 68°$, $p = 112°$
d) $s = 20°$, $t = 90°$

Q3 **a)** $x = 96°$, $p = 38°$
b) $a = 108°$, $b = 23°$, $c = 95°$
c) $d = 120°$, $e = 60°$, $f = 60°$, $g = 120°$
d) $h = 155°$, $i = 77.5°$, $j = 102.5°$, $k = 77.5°$

18

Answers: P.106 — P.110

Q4   **a)** $b = 70°$ $c = 30°$
         $d = 50°$ $e = 60°$
         $f = 150°$
   b) $g = 21°$ $h = 71°$
         $i = 80°$ $j = 38°$
         $k = 92°$
   c) $l = 35°$ $m = 145°$
         $n = 55°$ $p = 125°$

Q5   **a)** $x = 162°$ $y = 18°$
   b) $x = 87°$ $y = 93°$
         $z = 93°$
   c) $a = 30°$ $2a = 60°$
         $5a = 150°$ $4a = 120°$

Q6   **a)** $a = 141°$, $b = 141°$, $c = 39°$,
         $d = 141°$, $e = 39°$
   b) $a = 47°$, $b = 47°$, $c = 133°$,
         $d = 43°$, $e = 43°$
   c) $m = 140°$, $n = 140°$, $p = 134°$,
         $q = 46°$, $r = 40°$

Circle Geometry P.106-P.108

Q1   **a)** 117.607 m^2
   b) $45.216 = 45$ m to 2 s.f.
   c) 46.5 m to 1 d.p.
   d) 14.152 cm^2 to 3 d.p.

Q2   **a)** Area = area of a full circle radius 10 cm.
       $A = \pi r^2 = 3.14 \times 10^2 = 314 \text{ cm}^2$.
       Circumference = $\pi \times D$
       $= 3.14 \times 20 = 62.8$ cm.
       Perimeter = $62.8 + 20 = 82.8$ cm
   b) Area = (area of a circle radius 15 cm) +
       (area of a rectangle 15×30 cm)
       $= (\pi \times 15^2) + (15 \times 30)$
       $= 1156.5 \text{ cm}^2$.
       Perimeter = (circumference of a full
       circle radius 15 cm) + 15 + 15
       $= (\pi \times 30) + 30 = 124.2$ cm.
   c) Area = outer semicircle – inner
       semicircle = 510.25 m^2.
       Perimeter = ½ circumference of larger
       circle + ½ circumference of smaller
       circle + 5 + 5
       $= ½ \times \pi \times 70 + ½ \times \pi \times 60 + 10$
       $= 214.1$ m.

Q3   Both 90°

Q4   **a)** 90° (angle in a semicircle)
   b) The angle at A = 90° (tangent and
       radius are perpendicular).
       The third angle in the triangle is
       $180 - 90 - 23 = 67°$ and so
       $x = 90 - 67 = 23°$.

Q5   **a)** $80/360 \times \pi(5^2) = 17.45 \text{ cm}^2$
   b) Area of triangle AOB =
       $\frac{1}{2} \times 5 \times 5 \times \sin 80 = 12.31 \text{ cm}^2$.
       Shaded Area = $17.45 - 12.31$
       $= 5.14 \text{ cm}^2$

Q6   **a)** BAD = 80° (opposite angle C in cyclic
       quadrilateral)
   b) EAB = $180 - 80 - 30 = 70°$

Q7   **a)** BD = 5 cm (as the tangents BD and CD
       are equal).
   b) Angle COD = 70°
       ($= 180° - (20° + 90°)$), since tangent
       CD meets radius OC at an angle of 90°.
   c) Angle COB = 140° (since angle BOD
       equals angle COD).
   d) Angle CAB = 70° (since the angle at
       the centre (COB) is twice the angle at
       the edge (CAB)).

Q8   **a)** BOE = 106° (angle at centre)
   b) OAE = $90 - 32 = 58°$
       (tangent and radius meet at 90°)
       so OEA = 58°
       (isosceles formed by two radii)
       so AOE = $180 - 2 \times 58 = 64°$
       (triangle sum)
       so ACE = $64 \div 2 = 32°$
       (angle at centre is twice angle at edge)

Q9   **a)** CAD = $90 - 70 = 20°$
       (tangent and radius meet at 90°)
       ADC = 90° (angle in a semicircle)
       So ACD = $180 - 90 - 20 = 70°$
       (triangle sum)
   b) BAD = $180 - (30 + 70) = 80°$
       (opposite angles of a cyclic
       quadrilateral total 180°)

Q10   **a)** They are angles in the same segment.
    b) $3x + 40 = 6x - 50$
        $90 = 3x$
        $30 = x$
        angle ABD = $3(30) + 40 = 130°$

Q11   There are 2 ways of answering this
       question.

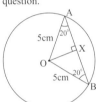

Diameter through O bisects the chord at X
so $\cos 20° = \frac{AX}{5}$
AX = 4.698 and
AB = 9.40 cm.

or by the sine rule $\frac{AB}{\sin 140} = \frac{5}{\sin 20}$

AB = $\frac{5 \sin 140}{\sin 20} = 9.40$ cm

Q12   **a)** Angle ABD = 70°
       (angle at centre = 2 × angle at edge)
    b) Angle ABC = 90° (angle in semicircle)
    c) Angle DBC = 20° ($90° - 70°$)

Q13   **a)** With AD as a chord, angle
       ABD = ACD = 30° (same segment);
       angle AXB = 85° (vertically opposite
       angles). The third angles must be the
       same in both triangles so the triangles
       must be similar.
    b) Ratio of lengths = $\frac{4}{8} = \frac{1}{2}$
       so XB = 5 cm
    c) angle BDC = $180 - 85 - 30 = 65°$

Q14   **a)** 90° (angle in a semicircle)
    b) Using Pythagoras:
       $AC^2 + 3^2 = 10^2$
       $AC^2 = 100 - 9 = 91$
       AC = 9.54 cm
    c) AD = 5 cm so DC = $9.54 - 5 = 4.54$ cm
       then Pythagoras gives
       $(4.54)^2 + 3^2 = (DOB)^2$
       $20.606 + 9 = (DOB)^2$
       So DOB = 5.44 cm

Pythagoras' Theorem and Bearings P.109-P.110

Q1   **a)** 10.8 cm   **f)** 7.89 m
   b) 6.10 m   **g)** 9.60 cm
   c) 5 cm   **h)** 4.97 cm
   d) 27.0 mm   **i)** 6.80 cm
   e) 8.49 m   **j)** 8.5 cm

Q2   a = 3.32 cm   f = 8.62 m
   b = 6 cm   g = 6.42 m
   c = 6.26 cm   h = 19.2 mm
   d = 5.6 m   i = 9.65 m
   e = 7.08 mm   j = 48.7 mm

Q3   k = 6.55 cm   q = 7.07 cm
   l = 4.87 m   r = 7.50 m
   m = 6.01 m   s = 9.45 mm
   n = 12.4 cm   t = 4.33 cm
   p = 5.22 cm   u = 7.14 m

Q4   **a)** 245°
   b) 310°
   c) 035°
   d) 131°
   e) 297°, 028°, 208°
   f) 139°, 284°, 104°

Q5   9.7 m

Q6   314 m

Q7   **a)** 12 cm, 7.94 cm
   b) 40.9 cm
   c) 89.7 cm^2

Q8   192 km

Q9   **a)**

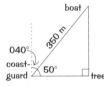

     i) 268 m
     ii) 225 m
   b) $350^2 = 122\,500$.
      $225^2 + 268^2 = 122\,449$

Q10

   a) 96 km
   b) 255 km
   c) 266 km
   d) 156°
   e) 082°
   f) 177°

Q11

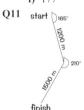

2500 m, 010°

SECTION SIX — ANGLES AND GEOMETRY

Q12

13.9 km from the starting point.
150° to return to base.

Trigonometry P.111-P.113

	(tan)	(sin)	(cos)
Q1 a)	0.306	0.292	0.956
b)	8.14	0.993	0.122
c)	0.0875	0.0872	0.996
d)	0.532	0.469	0.883
e)	1	0.707	0.707

Q2 a = 1.40 cm
b = 6 cm
θ = 28.1°
c = 5.31 cm
d = 10.8 cm

Q3 e = 12.6 cm
f = 11.3 cm
θ = 49.5°
g = 6.71 m
h = 30.1 cm

Q4 i = 4.89 cm
j = 3.79 cm
θ = 52.4°
k = 5.32 cm
l = 41.6 cm

Q5 m = 11.3 cm
n = 18.8 cm
p = 8.62 cm
q = 21.3 cm
r = 54.6°
t = 59.8 cm
u = 14.5 cm
v = 11.7 cm
w = 11.7 cm

Q6 a)

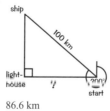

b) 36.9°

Q7 a)

b) 59.0°
c) 31.0°

Q8 a)

b) 71.6°   **c)** 36.9°   **d)** 71.5°

Q9 2.1 m
Q10 62°
Q11 20.5°
Q12

θ = 52.1°, bearing = 220 − 52 = 322°

Q13 a) both 30.8 cm
b) 27.5 cm   **c)** 385 cm²

Q14

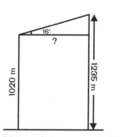

height = 5.90, base = 7.52,
so area = 22.2 cm².

Q15 a) 8.23 cm
b) 4.75 cm   **c)** 39.1 cm²

Q16 a) 10.8 cm
b) 150.8 cm²   **c)** 21.0°

Q17

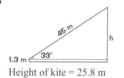

Distance between mountains = 750 m

Q18

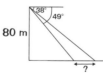

Height of kite = 25.8 m

Q19

a) 102.4 m, 69.5 m
b) 32.9 m

Q20

86.6 km

3D Pythagoras and Trigonometry
P.114

Q1 a) 59.0°
b) 23.3 cm
c) 25 cm
d) 21.1°

Q2 a) 42.5 cm
b) 50.9 cm

Q3 a) 36.1 cm, 21.5 cm, 31.0 cm
b) 36.9 cm

Q4 a) 15.4 cm
b) 20.4 cm

Q5 The 85p box

Q6 a) 3.82 cm
b) 45.8 cm²
c) 137.5 cm³

The Sine and Cosine Rules
P.115-P.117

Q1	a = 4.80 cm	f = 5.26 cm
	b = 25.8 mm	g = 9.96 cm
	c = 13.0 cm	h = 20.2 mm
	d = 8.89 m	i = 3.72 m
	e = 18.4 cm	j = 8.29 cm
Q2	k = 51°	q = 36°
	l = 46°	r = 64°
	m = 43°	s = 18°
	n = 53°	t = 49°
	p = 45°	u = 88°
Q3	a = 63°	i = 5.0 mm
	b = 45°	j = 68°
	c = 8.9 cm	k = 203 mm
	d = 27°	l = 127 mm
	e = 10.5 cm	m = 24.1 cm
	g = 49°	n = 149°
	h = 78°	p = 16°

Q4 a) 46°
b) 52°   c) 82°

Q5 12.0 m

Q6 a) 28.8 km   b) 295.5°

Q7

base = 7.04 cm

base = 8.39 cm

Q8

Distance = 1.2 miles.
The alarm should be ringing because the planes are less than 3 miles apart, so the software seems reliable.

Answers: P.117 — P.124

Q9

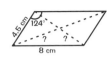

Diagonals 11.2 cm and 6.6 cm.

Q10
a) 16.9 m
b) 12.4 m
c) 25.8 m
d) 19.5 m

Q11

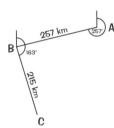

a) 86°
b) 323 km
c) 215°

Q12 a)

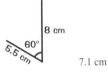

7.1 cm

b)

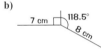

14.5 cm
(118.5° comes from the fact that the minute hand is at 19.75 mins. (19.75 ÷ 60) × 360 = 118.5.)

c)

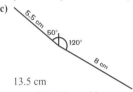

13.5 cm

Q13 Height of building = 35 m

Q14

Mary's string = 5.85 m
Jane's string = 7.13 m

Sine and Cosine for Larger Angles P.118

Q1
$a = 5.7$ cm $e = 13$ cm
$B = 38.9°$ $F = 62.6°$
$c = 8.2$ cm $G = 115.4°$
$D = 140°$

Q2
a) 122.9°
b) 135.6°   c) 170°

Q3 32.1 m

Q4
a) 109°
b) i) 28.5 m   ii) 107.6 m
c) 24.2 m

Q5 27.4 km
Q6 42.5° and 137.5°
Q7 153.5°

Section Seven

Mean, Median, Mode and Range P.119-P.120

Q1 3 tries

Q2
mean = 1.333 (to 3 d.p.)
median = 1.5
mode = 2
range = 11

Q3
a) mean = £12,944, or £13,000 to the nearest £500
median = £12,000
mode = £7,500
b) mode
c) E.g. mean — they should use the highest value to attract people to the job.

Q4
a) 0 minutes
b) 0 minutes
c) 0 minutes
d) No, according to the raw data.

Q5 73.5 kg
Q6 20 kg
Q7 97%
Q8 a) 22   b) 74
Q9
a) 3.5
b) 3.5   c) 5

Q10
a) Both spend a mean of 2 hours.
b) The range for Jim is 3 hours and for Bob is 2 hours.
c) E.g. The amount of TV that Jim watches each night is more variable than the amount that Bob watches.

Q11
a) 1 day   b) 2 days
c) The statement is true according to the data.

Q12 a) mode   b) mean

Sampling Methods P.121

Q1
a) Individuals are equally likely to be selected.
b) Start with a random selection and then select every, say, 10th or 100th one after that.
c) The population is divided into "strata" or "layers" – groups that don't overlap, like age ranges or sexes. Individuals are then randomly selected from each of the strata.

Q2
a) People in a newsagents are likely to be there to buy a newspaper.
b) At that time on a Sunday, people who go to church are likely to be at church.
c) The bridge club is unlikely to be representative of the population as a whole.

Q3
c) is the only suitable question as it is the only one which will always tell you which of the five desserts people like the most.

Q4
a) Do you play any team sports outside school?
Do you take part in any individual sports outside school?
Do you do any exercise at all outside school?
b) Pick at random 15 girls and 15 boys from each year.

Q5
a) E.g.:

Café Questionnaire
1) Please tick the box to show how often you visit the café:
daily ☐ weekly ☐ fortnightly ☐ monthly ☐ less than monthly ☐
2) Please tick the box to show how often you buy cola:
daily ☐ weekly ☐ fortnightly ☐ monthly ☐ less than monthly ☐

b) She will miss out the people who just buy drinks from the hot and cold drinks machines.

Frequency Tables P.122-P.123

Q1 a) 12   b) 12

Q2 a)

Subject	M	E	F	A	S
Frequency	5	7	3	4	6

b) 36 French lessons
c) English

Q3

Length (m)	4 and under	6	8	10	12	14 and over
Frequency	3	5	6	4	1	1

a) 8 m
b) 8 m   c) 14 m

Q4

Weight (kg)	Frequency	Weight × Frequency
51	40	2040
52	30	1560
53	45	2385
54	10	540
55	5	275

a) 52 kg
b) 53 kg
c) 52 kg (to nearest kg)

Q5
mean = 3.75
mode = 3
median = 4

Q6
a) 4
b) 3   c) 3.2 (to 1 dp)

Q7
a) i) False, mode is 8.
ii) False, they are equal.
iii) True
b) iv)

Grouped Frequency Tables P.124

Q1 a)

Speed (km/h)	40≤s<45	45≤s<50	50≤s<55	55≤s<60	60≤s<65
Frequency	4	8	10	7	3
Mid-Interval	42.5	47.5	52.5	57.5	62.5
Frequency × Mid-Interval	170	380	525	402.5	187.5

Estimated mean = 52 km/h
(to nearest km/h)

b) 22 skiers   c) 20 skiers

Answers: P.125 — P.127

Q2 **a)**

Weight (kg)	Tally	Frequency	Mid-Interval	Frequency × Mid-Interval
200 ≤ w < 250	IIII	4	225	900
250 ≤ w < 300	ЖЖ	5	275	1375
300 ≤ w < 350	ЖЖ II	7	325	2275
350 ≤ w < 400	II	2	375	750

b) 294 kg (to nearest kg)
c) $300 \leqslant w < 350$ kg

Q3 **a)**

Number	0≤n<0.2	0.2≤n<0.4	0.4≤n<0.6	0.6≤n<0.8	0.8≤n<1
Tally	ЖЖ ЖЖ II	ЖЖ I	ЖЖ II	ЖЖ	ЖЖ III
Frequency	12	6	12	10	8
Mid-Interval	0.1	0.3	0.5	0.7	0.9
Frequency × Mid-Interval	1.2	1.8	6	7	7.2

b) $0 \leqslant n < 0.2$ and $0.4 \leqslant n < 0.6$
c) $0.4 \leqslant n < 0.6$
d) 0.483 (3 dp)

Histograms and Frequency Density P.125-P.126

Q1 $4 \times 10 = 40$ people

Q2 **a)**

Weight (kg)	0≤w<2	2≤w<4	4≤w<7	7≤w<9	9≤w<15
Frequency	3	2	6	9	12
Frequency density	1.5	1	2	4.5	2

b)
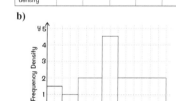

c) 23 hives

Q3 **a)**

Salary (£1000s)	0 ≤ s < 10	10 ≤ s < 20	20 ≤ s < 30	30 ≤ s < 40	40 ≤ s < 50
Frequency	10	25	42	20	3
Frequency Density	1	2.5	4.2	2	0.3

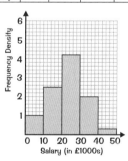

b) E.g. there are more people with higher salaries now than 10 years ago.

Q4 **a)**

No. of hours	Frequency	Frequency density
0 ≤ h < 1	6	6
1 ≤ h < 3	13	6.5
3 ≤ h < 5	15	7.5
5 ≤ h < 8	9	3
8 ≤ h < 10	23	11.5
10 ≤ h < 15	25	5
15 ≤ h < 20	12	2.4

b) 103 students

c)
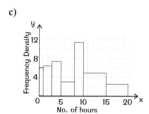

d) 41 students

Q5 **a)**

Amount of Milk (Litres)	Frequency	Frequency Density	Mid-Interval	Frequency × Mid-Interval
0 < C < 1	6	6	0.5	3
1 < C < 5	6	1.5	3	18
5 < C < 8	6	2	6.5	39
8 < C < 10	6	3	9	54
10 < C < 15	6	1.2	12.5	75
15 < C < 20	6	1.2	17.5	105

b) 8.2 litres (to 1 d.p.)

c)
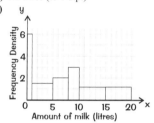

d) 18 days

Q6 **a)**

Amount (£)	Frequency	Frequency Density	Mid-Interval	Frequency × Mid-Interval
0 ≤ A < 0.50	11	22	0.25	2.75
0.50 ≤ A < 1.00	25	50	0.75	18.75
1.00 ≤ A < 1.30	9	30	1.15	10.35
1.30 ≤ A < 1.50	12	60	1.40	16.80
1.50 ≤ A < 1.80	24	80	1.65	39.60
1.80 ≤ A < 2.50	21	30	2.15	45.15
2.50 ≤ A < 3.10	54	90	2.80	151.20
3.10 ≤ A < 4.10	32	32	3.60	115.20

mean = £2.13 (to nearest penny)
b) $2.50 \leqslant A < 3.10$
c)
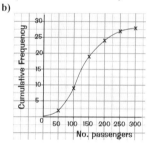

$(0.5 \times 22) + (0.5 \times 50)$
$+ (0.3 \times 30) + (0.1 \times 60)$
$= 51$ readers
d) No. 51 readers receive less than £1.40. So $188 - 51 = 137$ receive £1.40 or more. But 75% of 188 = 141.

Cumulative Frequency P.127-P.128

Q1 accept:
a) 133-134   **c)** 136-137
b) 127-128   **d)** 8-10

Q2

No. Sheep	0 ≤ s < 5	5 ≤ s < 10	10 ≤ s < 15	15 ≤ s < 20	20 ≤ s < 25	25 ≤ s < 30
Frequency	3	9	14	7	4	2
Cumulative Frequency	3	12	26	33	37	39

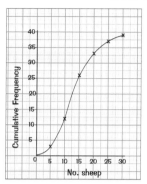

a) 12.5 (±1)
b) 9 (±1)
c) 17 (±1)
d) 8 (±2)
e) 16.5 (±2)
f) The interquartile range is smaller than the P_{90} to P_{10} percentile range. This means the data is fairly tightly distributed around the median.

Q3 **a)**

No. passengers	0≤n<50	50≤n<100	100≤n<150	150≤n<200	200≤n<250	250≤n<300
Frequency	2	7	10	5	3	1
Cumulative Frequency	2	9	19	24	27	28
Mid-Interval	25	75	125	175	225	275
Frequency × Mid-Interval	50	525	1250	875	675	275

Estimated mean = 130 passengers (to nearest whole number)

b)
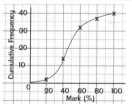

accept median of 118-122 passengers
c) $100 \leqslant n < 150$

Q4 **a)**

Mark (%)	0 ≤ m < 20	20 ≤ m < 40	40 ≤ m < 60	60 ≤ m < 80	80 ≤ m < 100
Frequency	2	12	18	5	3
Cumulative Frequency	2	14	32	37	40

b) 36%-38%
c) 19%-21%
d) 45%-47%

Q5

Score	31≤s<41	41≤s<51	51≤s<61	61≤s<71	71≤s<81	81≤s<91	91≤s<101
Frequency	4	12	21	32	19	8	4
Cumulative Frequency	4	16	37	69	88	96	100

a) $61 \leqslant s < 71$
b) $61 \leqslant s < 71$
c)

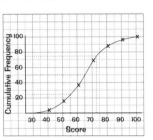

median = 65 (accept 64-66)
d) 73 – 55 = 18 (accept 17-19)

Q6

a)

Life (hours)	Frequency	Cumulative Frequency
900 ≤ L < 1000	10	10
1000 ≤ L < 1100	12	22
1100 ≤ L < 1200	15	37
1200 ≤ L < 1300	18	55
1300 ≤ L < 1400	22	77
1400 ≤ L < 1500	17	94
1500 ≤ L < 1600	14	108
1600 ≤ L < 1700	9	117

b) $1300 \leqslant L < 1400$
c)

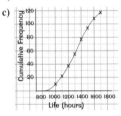

median = 1320 hours (±20)
d) lower quartile = 1150 (±20)
upper quartile = 1460 (±20)

Q7

a)

Time	2:00≤t<2:30	2:30≤t<3:00	3:00≤t<3:30	3:30≤t<4:00	4:00≤t<4:30
Tally	I	IIII	IIII IIII IIII	IIII II	III
Frequency	1	5	14	7	3
Cumulative Frequency	1	6	20	27	30

b)

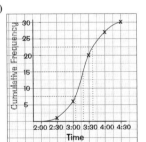

c) median = 3:19 (±3)
upper quartile = 3:37 (±3)
lower quartile = 3:05 (±3)
d) 0:32 (±5)

Spread of Data P.129

Q1 (A,I), (B,II)
Q2 A — 16 year olds
B — bags of sugar

Q3 **a)** The chart shows a tight distribution of data, with most of the values falling in a narrow range close to the mean.
b) The chart shows a wide spread of data.
c) Chart B represents the age of the UK population as it shows a wider spread of data.

Scatter Graphs P.130-P.131

Q1 (A,S), (B,R), (C,P), (D,U)
Q2 **a)**

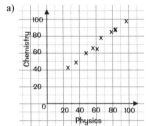

b) There is no correlation.
c) No — if he were correct the graph would show negative correlation.
Q3 **a)**

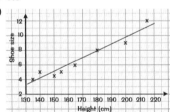

b) Strong positive correlation.
c) Yes
Q4 **a)**

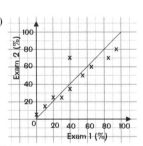

b) Positively correlated.
c) The greater the height, the bigger the shoe size.
d) 9
Q5 **a), b)**

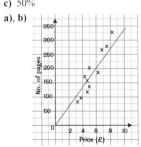

c) 50%
Q6 **a), b)**

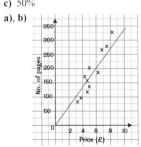

c) £7.50 (±20p)

Q7 **a)**

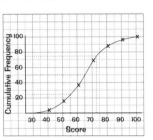

b) i) 20 (to nearest whole number)
ii) £140 (± £10)
c) The data is negatively correlated.

Stem and Leaf Diagrams P.132

Q1 3, 3, 3, 5, 8, 8, 9, 12, 13, 14, 14, 18, 18, 19, 20, 22, 22, 24, 31, 33.
Q2 **a)** 2   **e)** 21
b) 4   **f)** 21.24
c) 6   **g)** 21
d) 39
Q3
```
0 | 7 8
1 | 1 3 5 8
2 | 1 2 3 6 9
3 | 1 3 7 9
4 | 1 8
5 | 0
```
Q4
```
40 | 1 2
35 | 0 0 1 1 1 2 3 3 4
30 | 0 0 0 0 0 0 0 0 0 0 1 1 1 1 1 1 1 1 2 2 2 2 2 3 3 3 3 4 4 4 4
25 | 0 0 0 0 0 1 1 1 1 1 1 2 2 2 2 2 3 3 3 3 3 3 3 4 4 4 4 4 4 4 4 4
20 | 1 3 3 4 4 4 4
```
E.g. Key: 20|1 means 21

Pie Charts P.133

Q1 $\frac{360°}{100} = 3.6°$ per gram

Carbohydrate	$3.6 \times 35 = 126°$
Protein	$3.6 \times 15 = 54°$
Fat	$3.6 \times 10 = 36°$
Magical Fairy Dust	$3.6 \times 40 = \underline{144°}$

Q2 Sherrington 380,000 = 148°
(approx) 2600 visitors = 1°
So, to the nearest 10,000:
Brompton = 2600 × 118° ≈ 310,000
Barny = 2600 × 44° ≈ 110,000
Livsea = 2600 × 50° ≈ 130,000
Q3 Part c)
Q4 It's not possible to tell whether more women like apple pies than men, because you can't tell how many people were questioned in either article.

Answers: P.134 — P.140

Other Graphs and Charts
P.134-P.135

Q1

	Van	Motor-bike	Car	Truck	Total
Travelling North	3	2	62	5	72
Travelling South	10	0	0	3	13
Travelling East	7	2	26	4	39
Travelling West	1	3	31	1	36
Total	21	7	119	13	160

a) 62   **c)** 1
b) 7   **d)** 7

Q2   **a)** 58
   b) 7
   c) 4 more people liked cola best; 7 less people liked cherryade best.
   d) e.g. Cola was the most popular and milk the least popular / cola was much more popular than milk.

Q3   **a)** E.g.   **i)** She only asked her friends
       ii) She only asked 1 set
       iii) The sample was too small
   b) Discrete
   c)

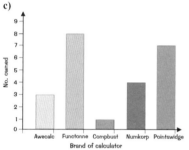

Q4   **a)**

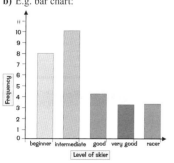

   b) 72 children   **c)** 9 children
   d) Rounders — it's the most popular

Q5   **a)** E.g. tally chart:

Level of skier	No.
Beginner	卌 III
Intermediate	卌 卌
Good	IIII
Very good	II
Racer	II

   b) E.g. bar chart:

c) Most common type of skier is Intermediate.

Q6 The statement is not correct.
Complaints have not "tailed off" - they have remained the same (approx 10,850) per month.
The number of complaints is not increasing but there are still 10,850 per month, every month.
The products cannot possibly be improving in quality if the complaints remain the same each month.

Probability P.136-P.140

Q1   **a)** 1/2   **c)** 1/6
   b) 2/3   **d)** 0

And so should be arranged <u>approximately</u> like this on the number line:

Q2 Debbie's chance of winning would be 1/9. This is greater than 0.1, so she would choose to play.

Q3 The probability of a head is still 1/2

Q4 $1 - 0.27 = 0.73$ or $73/100$

Q5   **a)** 5/12
   b) 4/12 = 1/3
   c) 3/12 = 1/4
   d) 9/12 = 3/4

Q6   **a)** 40/132 = 10/33
   b) P(car being blue or green) = 45/132
     P(not blue or green) = 87/132
     = 29/44

Q7   **a)** 1/4
   b) $1/4 \times 100$ = approx 25 days

Q8   **a)**

Outcome	Frequency
W	8
D	5
L	7

   b) The 3 outcomes are not equally likely.
   c) 5/20 = 1/4
   d) They are most likely to win.

Q9   **a)** $\frac{1}{13}$ **b)** $\frac{2}{39}$ **c)** $\frac{1}{36}$

Q10   **a)** $\frac{7}{12}$ **b)** $\frac{7}{12}$
   c) The two are not mutually exclusive (or other equivalent answer).

Q11   **a)** $\frac{2}{5}$ **b)** $\frac{4}{15}$ **c)** $\frac{2}{3}$

Q12   **a)** $\frac{7}{20} = 0.35$ **b)** $\frac{2}{5} = 0.4$
   c) Best estimate will be from the experiment with the most dice rolls, so it will be 0.4.

Q13   **a)** $\frac{11}{150}$ **b)** $\frac{1}{20}$
   c) The red dice is probably biased, as if you rolled an unbiased dice 250 times you would expect each of the 10 numbers to come up 25 times. On the red dice, 10 came up 33 times, which is 8 more than you'd expect.

Q14   **a)** (1,1), (1,2), (1,3), (1,4), (1,5), (1,6), (1,7), (2,1), (2,2), (2,3), (2,4), (2,5), (2,6), (2,7), (3,1), (3,2), (3,3), (3,4), (3,5), (3,6), (3,7)
   b)

	1	2	3	4	5	6	7
1	2	3	4	5	6	7	8
2	3	4	5	6	7	8	9
3	4	5	6	7	8	9	10

   c) $\frac{1}{7}$ **d)** $\frac{11}{21}$
   e) $\frac{2}{7}$ **f)** $\frac{5}{7}$
   g) Subtract the answer to part **e)** from 1.

Q15   **a)** 8   **b)** 40   **c)** 43/80
   d) They'd get closer to 1/10 each.

Q16   **a)**

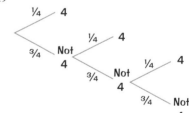

   b) $\frac{18}{35}$ **c)** $\frac{3}{7}$

Q17   **a)** $\frac{1}{13}$ **c)** $\frac{36}{143}$
   b) $\frac{83}{143}$ **d)** $\frac{6}{143}$

Q18 4 times

Q19

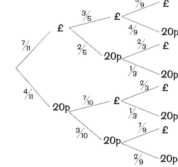

   a) $\frac{3}{16}$ **b)** $\frac{37}{64}$

Q20   **a)**

   b) $\frac{28}{55}$ **c)** $\frac{46}{165}$

Q21   **a)** $\frac{1}{4}$ **b)** $\frac{1}{2}$ **c)** $\frac{1}{2}$

Q22 $\frac{1}{28}$

SECTION SEVEN — HANDLING DATA

ISBN 978 1 84762 559 5

9 781847 625595

MIAI41

CGP

Key Stage Three
Biology, Physics & Chemistry

Answer Book

For the **Foundation Level** Workbooks

Contents

Biology

Chemistry

Physics

Published by CGP

Compiled by Paddy Gannon

ISBN: 978 1 84146 894 5

www.cgpbooks.co.uk

Printed by Elanders Ltd, Newcastle upon Tyne.
Clipart from Corel®

Answers

Biology

Section 1 — Cells and Respiration

Pages 1-2 — The Microscope

Q1   A — Eyepiece lens
B — Rough focusing knob
C — High and low power objective lenses
D — Stage

Q2 a) False
b) True
c) False
d) True
e) False
f) False

Q3 a) The mirror.
b) lowest powered
c) The rough focusing knob.
d) Jessica should stop moving the lens down when it is just **above** the slide.

Q4 a) The fine focusing knob.
b) Use a higher powered objective lens.

Pages 3-5 — Cells

Q1 a) A – nucleus
B – cell membrane
C – cell wall
D – mitochondria
E – vacuole
F – cytoplasm
G – chloroplasts

b)

Animal and plant cells have	Only plant cells have
1) cell membrane	1) cell wall
2) nucleus	2) chloroplasts
3) cytoplasm	3) vacuole
4) mitochondria	

Q2   Chloroplast — where photosynthesis happens.
Vacuole — large space filled with sap.
Mitochondria — where aerobic respiration happens.
Cytoplasm — a jelly where most of the chemical reactions happen.
Nucleus — controls what the cell does.
Cell membrane — thin skin around the cell.
Cell wall — stiff outer layer which gives support to the cell.

Q3 a) Because they are really small / too small to see with just your eyes.

b)

	Cytoplasm	Nucleus	Cell wall	Vacuole
Animal cheek cell	✓	✓		
Plant leaf cell	✓	✓	✓	✓

c) It holds the cell together and controls what goes in and out of the cell.

Q4 a) salts and sugars.
b) no

Q5 a) Has only one cell.
b) E.g. animal / plant / human.
c) It helps it to swim in water.

Page 6 — Cell Organisation

Q1 a) tissue, organ, organ ~~system, organism~~
b) cells

Q2 a) Diffusion
b) Oxygen molecules will move **into** the cell. This is because there are more oxygen molecules **outside** the cell.

Pages 7-10 — Respiration

Q1   Inside **every** cell in your body **glucose** is used to release **energy**. This process is called **respiration**. All living things need energy for everything, including building **proteins** and keeping **warm**.

Q2 a) The process of releasing energy from glucose.
b) chemical
c) Aerobic and anaerobic.

Q3   Uses glucose — Both aerobic and anaerobic
Produces water — Aerobic only
Releases energy — Both aerobic and anaerobic
Uses oxygen — Aerobic only

Q4 a) Glucose and oxygen.
b) Carbon dioxide and water.
c) Energy
d) B + C → A + D + E (the letters can be in any order, as long as they are on the right side of the arrow.)

Q5   glucose → lactic acid + energy
glucose → carbon dioxide + ethanol + energy

Q6 a) To release energy.
b) Tim's body will get more glucose that can be used to release more energy which can be used to run with.
c) Anaerobic respiration is respiration without oxygen.
d) hard exercise

Q7 a) glucose
b) anaerobic
c) The yeast must respire anaerobically, so they must be kept away from the oxygen in the air.
d) fermentation

Q8 a) aerobic
b) anaerobic
c) aerobic
d) anaerobic

Q9 a) aerobic respiration
b) ethanol
c) energy
d) carbon dioxide
e) water
f) oxygen
g) glucose
h) anaerobic respiration
i) lactic acid
j) fermentation

Answers

Section 2 — Humans as Organisms

Pages 11-12 — Nutrition

Q1 Vitamins — To keep many important processes happening in your body.
Carbohydrates — For energy. You need lots of these if you're active or growing.
Lipids (fats and oils) — For storing energy for if your body runs out of carbohydrates.
Proteins — For growth and to repair damage.

Q2 a) mineral
b) E.g. it is needed for strong bones/teeth.
c) E.g. milk

Q3 A diet with the right amounts of nutrients, fibre and water.

Q4 a) Bread
b) Fibre helps food move through your digestive system.
c) E.g. vegetables / fruit

Q5 a) E.g. iron, it is needed for healthy blood.
b) E.g. eggs

Q6 E.g. all chemical reactions in the body take place in water.

Pages 13-14 — More on Nutrition

Q1 All the time

Q2 a) i) If you take in **more** energy than you use up, you will **put on** weight. Over time, you could become obese.
ii) E.g. heart disease
b) E.g. slow growth in children / irregular periods in women.

Q3 a) Carbohydrates and lipids/fats/oils.
b) i) The **heavier** you are, the more energy you will need each day.
ii) E.g. how active you are.

Q4 a) Not having enough vitamins or minerals in your diet.
b) E.g. It can cause skin / gum problems.

Q5 Daily BER (kJ/day) = 5.4 × 24 × body mass (kg)
Mihir's BER = 5.4 × 24 × 65
= **8424 kJ/day**

Q6 7776 + 3000 = 10 776 kJ

Pages 15-16 — Digestion

Q1 Brain and lung should be crossed.

Q2 **Digestion** is the breakdown of **food** so we can use the **nutrients** it contains. Special chemicals called **enzymes** are used to break food down. They **speed** up chemical reactions in the body.

Q3 a) The mouth
b) Pancreas and small intestine should be circled.

Q4 a) E.g. chewing food using your teeth. / The stomach muscles churning food.
b) enzymes

Q5 A — Liver — Makes bile to break up fats.
B — Pancreas — Contains tissue that makes enzymes.
C — Small intestine — Makes enzymes to break down proteins, carbohydrates and fats. Food is also absorbed from here.
D — Large intestine — Water is absorbed from here.

Q6 a) To kill harmful bacteria.
b) To move the stomach wall and churn up the food.
c) The gullet.

Pages 17-18 — More on Digestion

Q1 a) Small intestine
b) The body uses enzymes to **break up** big molecules into small ones. These smaller molecules can pass through the **wall** of the intestine. From here they travel around the body, then pass to **cells** in the body to be used.
c) The blood

Q2 a) villi
b) They have a thin outer layer of cells. They have a good blood supply. They provide a large surface area for absorption.

Q3 a) unicellular
b) Any three of e.g. They make enzymes to help you digest food. / They help stop harmful bacteria growing in your intestines (that could make you ill). / They make useful vitamins.

Pages 19-21 — The Skeleton and Muscles

Q1 The b**ones** in your skeleton protect many important o**rgans** in your body. Bones also allow m**ovement** to occur and **suppor**t the entire body.

Q2 a) B → D → C → A
b) E.g. The skull protects the brain.
c) They can't bend
d) White blood cells and red blood cells

Q3 a) i) B
ii) C
iii) A
b) Tendons
c) When a muscle **contracts**, it **pulls** on the bone it's attached to. This applies a force to the **bone**, which makes the bone **move**.

Q4 a) true
b) false
c) false

Q5 a) triceps
b) relaxed
c) Muscle A will contract, pulling the arm straight. As this happens the biceps muscle will relax.

Pages 22-23 — Gas Exchange

Q1 Lung — f
Trachea (windpipe) — a
Bronchus — c
Bronchiole — e
Alveoli (air sacs) — g
Diaphragm — h
Ribcage — b
Intercostal muscle — d

Q2 We need to take in **oxygen** from the **air** to stay alive. We also need to get rid of **carbon dioxide** from our bodies. This overall process is called **gas exchange**.

Q3 a) i) oxygen
ii) Respiration / releasing energy
b) i) carbon dioxide
ii) respiration

Answers

Q4 They're moist
They have a good blood supply
The alveoli give the lungs a large inside surface area

Pages 24-25 — Breathing
Q1 **a)** lungs
b) intercostal muscles and diaphragm
c) diaphragm
d) i) They fill with air.
ii) inhalation / breathing in
iii) When the rubber sheet is pulled down, the volume of the jar **increases**, so the pressure inside the jar **decreases**.

Q2 1. Intercostal muscles contract — Rib cage moves upwards and outwards
2. Diaphragm contracts — Diaphragm moves down
3. Volume of the chest increases — Air enters to fill the extra room
4. Intercostal muscles relax — Rib cage moves downwards and inwards
5. Diaphragm relaxes — Diaphragm moves upwards
6. Volume of the chest decreases — Air rushes out of the chest space

Q3 **a)** False
b) True
c) True
d) True

Q4 **a)** The amount/volume of air you can breathe into your lungs in a single breath.
b) E.g. Susan, because shorter people tend to have a smaller lung volume than taller people.

Page 26 — Exercise, Asthma and Smoking
Q1 **a) i)** You breathe **deeper** and **faster** when you exercise.
ii) To get more oxygen to your muscles.
b) It helps you to get more air into your lungs.
c) You develop more small blood vessels in your lungs / your lungs become better at absorbing oxygen into your blood.

Q2 **a)** They will contract.
b) E.g. the lining of the airways will become inflamed and fluid will build up.

Q3 **a)** **Cigarette** smoke contains tar. Tar **covers** the cilia in the airways. The damaged **cilia** can't get rid of **mucus** properly. It **sticks** to the airways, which makes you **cough** more.
b) E.g. lung diseases / cancer

Pages 27-28 — Human Reproduction
Q1 A — scrotum
B — testes
C — penis
D — foreskin
E — sperm duct
F — ovary
G — uterus/womb
H — vagina
I — Fallopian tube

Q2 **a)** sperm
b) To produce sperm.
c) egg
d) The ovaries
e) gametes

Q3 **a)** During sexual intercourse
b) The nucleus of the egg and the nucleus of the sperm must combine.
c) Fallopian tube

Q4 Every 28 days

Q5 **a)** The fertilised egg divides to become a ball of cells. This ball of cells is the embryo.
b) The womb/uterus
c) It breaks down and passes out of the vagina.

Pages 29-30 — The Menstrual Cycle
Q1 Each time an egg cell is released the **uterus** gets ready to receive a fertilised egg. The lining of the **uterus** gets **thick**. If the egg is fertilised, the egg will land there. If the egg is not **fertilised** the lining will **break down** and pass out of the **vagina**. This is called a **period**.

Q2 Stage 1 — Bleeding starts. The lining of the uterus breaks down.
Stage 2 — The lining of the uterus starts to build up.
Stage 3 — The egg is released.
Stage 4 — The lining of the uterus is maintained.

Q3 3 to 4 days

Q4 **a)** 1. D
2. B
3. C
4. A
b) Day 14
c) In case it receives a fertilised egg.

Pages 31-32 — Having a Baby
Q1 **a)** gestation
b) 1 month — The embryo has a brain, heart, eyes and legs.
5 months — The baby can kick its legs by now.
7 months — The baby would probably survive if it were born now.
39 weeks — The baby is ready to be born.
c) i) 9 weeks
ii) A foetus

Q2

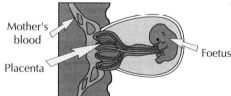

Mother's blood

Placenta

Foetus

Q3 **a)** E.g. The placenta lets the foetus get the things it needs from its mother's blood, e.g. food and oxygen.
b) i) E.g. drinking alcohol, taking drugs.
ii) They get into the mother's blood, then they cross the placenta to the baby.

workbook

Answers

Q4 **a)** False
b) False
c) True
d) True
Q5 All of the answers should be circled.

Pages 33-35 — Health and Drugs
Q1 **a)** Growth — getting to adult size
Nutrition — getting food to stay alive
Respiration — turning food into energy
Excretion — getting rid of waste
Movement — moving parts of the body
Sensitivity — responding and reacting
Reproduction — producing offspring
Q2 A drug is anything that affects the way your body works.
Q3 **a)** Any two from, e.g. beer, wine, spirits.
b) sensitivity
Q4 **a)** True
b) True
c) False
d) True
e) True
Q5 **a)** They will make you feel like you need to have them.
b) Both illegal and legal drugs can affect your behaviour.
c) E.g. heroin / LSD
Q6 Drinking alcohol and then driving is very dangerous. Alcohol **decreases** your **brain** activity, which means you react to things more **slowly**. It also affects your **judgement**, which means you might end up making silly decisions.
Q7

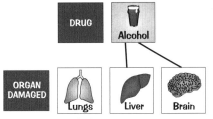

Q8 **a)** E.g. paints and glue.
b) i) Makes you see things that are not really there
Affects your behaviour
ii) Can damage the lungs
Can damage the brain

Section 3 — Plants and Ecosystems
Pages 36-39 — Plant Nutrition
Q1 **a)** carbon dioxide + **water** → **glucose** + **oxygen**
b) i) carbon dioxide and water
ii) glucose and oxygen
c) carbohydrate
Q2 1. (sun)light
2. chlorophyll
3. water
4. carbon dioxide
Q3 **a)** carbon dioxide
b) oxygen

Q4

Q5 **a)** The soil.
b) The roots.
Q6 **a)** Both plants were watered regularly.
b) Repeat the experiment several times with other plants.
c) i) it will die
ii) These two experiments tell Tom that plants need **sunlight** and **water** to survive.
Q7 Leaves are flat and wide — so they have a big surface area for absorbing light.
Leaves have lots of chloroplasts that are mainly near the upper surface — so as much light as possible reaches the chloroplasts.
Leaves have tiny holes (stomata) in the lower surface — so carbon dioxide and oxygen can move in and out easily.

Pages 40-42 — Plant Reproduction
Q1 The **male** sex cell is produced by the pollen, and the **female** sex cell is contained in the **ovule**.
Q2 **a)**

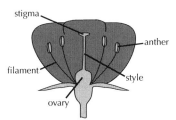

b) i) The carpel / female reproductive system.
ii) The ovules / female sex cells.
c) i) The stamen / male reproductive system.
ii) The pollen / male sex cells.
d) To attract insects to pollinate the flower.
Q3 The female sex cell in plants is contained inside — the ovule.
The female sex organ in plants is called — the carpel.
The female sex organ is made up from — the stigma, style and ovary.
The male sex cell in plants is produced by — the pollen.
The male sex organ in plants is called — the stamen.
The male sex organ is made up from — the filament and anther.

Answers

Q4 The extra words to find are: stamen, carpel

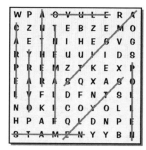

Q5 a) During pollination, **pollen grains** travel from a **stamen** to a **stigma**. This allows male and female **sex cells** to meet up and make a **seed**. Plants can be pollinated by **insects** or **wind**.

b) i) B
ii) feathery stigmas, long anthers hanging outside the flower

c) i) A
ii) 4 — Pollen is pulled off the insect by a sticky stamen in the second flower.
1 — The insect visits the first flower to get food.
3 — Pollen is carried by the insect when it travels to the second flower.
2 — Pollen sticks to the insect.

Pages 43-44 — Fertilisation and Seed Formation

Q1 Fertilisation in plants is **the joining of sex cells**.

Q2 A **pollen grain** lands on a **stigma** with help from insects or the wind. A **pollen tube** then grows out of the pollen grain into the **ovary**. The **nucleus** from a male **sex cell** inside the pollen grain moves down the tube. This nucleus joins with the **nucleus** of a **female** sex cell inside an **ovule**.

Q3 a) i) After fertilisation, the fertilised **ovule** develops into a **seed**.
ii) Each seed contains an **embryo plant**.
b) A fruit.

Q4 a) explosion, animal, drop and roll, wind
b) Burdock — Animal
The fruit has hooks that catch on animals' coats, so it gets carried away.
Sycamore — Wind
The fruit has wings to help carry it away from the parent tree.
Dandelion — Wind
The fruit has parachutes to help it catch the wind.
Pea — Explosion
The pod dries out and flicks the seeds out.
Tomato — Animal
The fruit gets eaten by an animal and the seeds come out in the animal's poo.

Pages 45-46 — Investigating Seed Dispersal

Q1 a) The person dropping the fruit
The height the fruit is dropped from
The place where the experiment takes place
b) i) Sycamore = (20 + 25 + 21) ÷ 3 = **22 cm**
ii) Elm = (18 + 14 + 16) ÷ 3 = **16 cm**

c) **Sycamore** fruits disperse further than **elm** fruits.

Q2 a) So the fruits aren't affected by other wind or draughts.
b) How far the fan is from where Jimmy drops the fruit.
The speed of the fan when it is switched on.
c) i) Sycamore fruits are dispersed **farther** when it is windy.
ii) 127 cm – 23 cm = **104 cm**

Pages 47-48 — Dependence on Other Organisms

Q1 a) the Sun
b) Plants use energy from the **Sun** to make **food** during **photosynthesis**. Plants use the food to build **molecules**, which store **energy**.
c) Animals **can't** use photosynthesis to capture and store the Sun's energy, but plants **can**. This means animals **need** plants to get energy. **Energy** is passed on from **plants** to **animals** when animals eat the plants.

Q2 a)

	Taken in	Given out
Respiration	oxygen	E.g. carbon dioxide
Photosynthesis	carbon dioxide	oxygen

b) i) carbon dioxide
ii) oxygen

Q3 a) All the living **organisms** in one area, plus their **environment**.
b) Interdependent means the organisms **need** each other to survive.

Q4 a) Many plants need insects to pollinate them.
b) We need **insects** to **pollinate** crop plants, so they can produce **fruit** and **seeds**. If insect numbers fall, **fewer** plants may be pollinated, so less food may be produced.

Pages 49-52 — Food Chains and Food Webs

Q1 a) E.g. food for
b) i) the limpet
ii) the lobster
iii) no
c) Energy is transferred along the food chain from the **algae** to the **lobster**.
d) i) consumer — an organism that eats other living things
producer — an organism that can make its own food
ii) algae
iii) limpet, lobster

Q2 primary consumer — An animal that eats producers
secondary consumer — An animal that eats primary consumers.
tertiary consumer — An animal that eats secondary consumers.

Q3 a) blackberry, grass
b) aphid, caterpillar, mouse, vole, rabbit
c) hawk
d) blackberry —> mouse —> owl

6

Answers

e) blackberry —> **aphid** —> **blue tit** —> hawk
blackberry —> **caterpillar** —> **blue tit** —> hawk
(These food chains can be given in either order.)

f) If the number of grass plants increased, the number of voles might **increase** because they would have **more** food.

g) i) The number of blue tits might **increase** because **fewer of them would be eaten.**
  ii) it could decrease

Q4 a) weasel, fox
  b i) Organisms at the top of the food chain.
   ii) The poison builds up as it's passed along the food chain.
  c) hawk

Section 4 — Inheritance, Variation and Survival

Page 53 — DNA and Inheritance

Q1 a) A — Nucleus
 B — Chromosome
 C — Gene
 D — DNA

  b) **Crick and Watson** were the first scientists to build a model of the DNA molecule. They showed that it is a **spiral** made up of two **chains**. They used data from two other scientists called **Wilkins and Franklin**.

Q2 a) heredity
  b) Genes control characteristics and offspring get a mixture of their parents' genes/genetic information.
  c) hereditary characteristics

Pages 54-56 — Variation

Q1 a) Differences between living things.
  b) Natasha looks different from the seal because they are **different** species.
  c) They have different genes/genetic information.
  d) **Variation** can happen within a **species**. For example, human beings have different skin colours. These **differences** are known as characteristic features.
  e) Natasha's natural hair colour — genes
 Natasha's tattoo — environment
 Rodney's haircut — environment

Q2 a) i) Discontinuous variation
   ii) The feature can only take certain values.
  b) Hair length — continuous variation
 Blood type — discontinuous variation
 Weight — continuous variation
 Skin colour — continuous variation
  c) Genes

Q3 a) Wrong, because the groups in the results form a continuous range, so height can take any value in a certain range.
  b) Height is a characteristic feature that **is** passed down from your parents in your genes. The food you eat **can also** affect how tall you grow. This means that height is a characteristic feature that is caused by **both genes and the environment.**

Pages 57-59 — Natural Selection and Survival

Q1 a) i) B. It has bigger claws than A, and twice as many claws as C. So lobster B will be better than A and C at catching food and defending itself.
   ii) Lobster C
  b) Lobsters which are most like **lobster B** would be more likely to survive. This means that they are more likely to **reproduce** and pass their **genes** on to their young. Gradually the whole population would become more and more like **lobster B**.
  c) Natural selection

Q2 a) Slow rabbits.
  b) E.g. slow rabbits are easier for the foxes to catch than fast rabbits therefore fewer of them get the chance to reproduce and pass on their genes than fast rabbits.
  c) In field A, **fast** rabbits are better at competing, so being **fast** becomes more common due to **natural selection**. In field B, **slow** rabbits are as likely to survive as fast rabbits and so they **don't die out**. So rabbits from field **A** are more likely to be fast.
  d) The rabbit from field A.

Q3 a) These should be circled: Other species that eat seals, other polar bears.
  b) They are less likely to survive and reproduce.
  c) They will get stronger.

Q4 There aren't enough fruit and seeds to go round.

Q5 1 — Organisms show variation because of differences in their genes.
2 — Some organisms have a useful characteristic that makes them better at competing than others in their species.
3 — These organisms are more likely to survive and reproduce.
4 — The organisms that survive pass on the genes for their useful characteristic to their offspring.
5 — Over time, the useful characteristic becomes more common.

Page 60 — Extinction and Preserving Species

Q1 a) When the trees in the rainforest are cut down to make room for fields, there is less **food** for gorillas to eat. Those gorillas that are less able to compete successfully for food will **struggle** to survive and **reproduce**.
  b) i) Extinct — None of that species are left.
   ii) Endangered — At risk of becoming extinct.

Q2 a) Medicine, clothing, fuels
  b) It might affect an organism that we make use of.

Q3 a) The variety of species.
  b) A store of genes of different species.
  c) E.g. A seed bank / store of seeds

Answers

Answers

Chemistry

Section 1 — Classifying Materials

Page 1 — Solids, Liquids and Gases
Q1 a) There are **three** states of matter.
b) Solids, liquids and gases have **different** properties.
c) **Solids** have a definite shape.
d) Liquids change **shape** depending on the container they're in.
e) **Solids** don't flow.
Q2 high density = solid
medium density = liquid
low density = gas
Q3 a) Solid
b) Gas
c) Liquid
Q4 Gas

Pages 2-4 — Particle Theory
Q1 a) true
b) false
c) false
d) true
e) true
Q2

	Particles are close together	Particles are free to move
Solid	✔	
Liquid	✔	✔
Gas		✔

Q3 Liquid — X, Solid — Z, Gas —Y
Q4 a) solid
b) The **weaker** the forces between the particles, the further apart the particles will be.
Q5 a) Yes
b) No
Q6 E.g. the particles are close together but able to move past each other.
Q7 In a solid, the particles are held very **close** together, although they do **vibrate** a bit. The particles can't **move** very much, so all solids keep the **same** shape and **volume** and can't **flow** like liquids. Solids can't easily be **squashed** because the particles are already very **close** together. Solids are usually **dense**, as there are lots of particles in a **small** volume.
Q8 The particles move quickly in all directions, there is lots of space between the particles, there are very weak forces between the particles.

Pages 5-8 — More Particle Theory
Q1 The arrangement of the particles and the energy of the particles
Q2 a) A — Solid   B — Liquid   C — Gas
b) D — Melting   F — Boiling
E — Freezing   G — Condensing

Q3 When a liquid is heated, the particles **gain** energy. This makes the particles move **faster**. This makes the forces between the particles **weaker**. At a certain **temperature**, the particles have enough energy to break the forces between them and the liquid turns into a **gas**. This is called **boiling**.
Q4 These should be ticked: c), e), f) and g).
Q5 melting and boiling
Q6 a) They get more energy.
b) The particles move faster, so the forces holding the particles together get weaker.
c) i) The distance between the particles increases.
ii) The energy of the particles increases.
Q7 The spreading out of **particles** is called **diffusion**. A smell spreading across a room is an example of this effect. The smell particles move from where there are **lots** of them to where there are **fewer** of them.
Q8 a) There should be lots of smell particles near the porridge and none anywhere else, e.g.

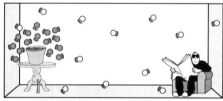

b) C

Pages 9-14 — Atoms and Elements
Q1 Elements are substances that **contain only one type of atom**.
Each element has **a name and symbol**.
The symbol for an element is made up of **one or two letters**.
Atoms are pretty much **the smallest, simplest types of particle**.
The periodic table contains **the symbols for all the elements**.
Q2 These should be ticked: carbon, nitrogen, oxygen, helium.
Q3

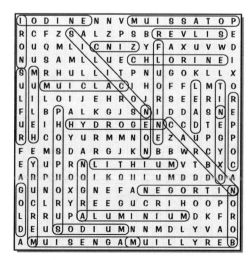

Q4 a) elements
b) A column of elements.

Answers

c)

1 2		3 4 5 6 7	8 or 0

d)   A row of elements.
e)   Metal
Q5   A, C, D, E, F, G
Q6 a)   Any three from, e.g. carbon (C), nitrogen (N), oxygen (O), iodine (I), hydrogen (H).
b)   potassium (K)
c)   Any two from, e.g. lithium (Li), beryllium (Be), neon (Ne), argon (Ar).
d)   Any two from, e.g. lead (Pb), gold (Au), mercury (Hg), sodium (Na).
e)   E.g. chlorine (Cl) / magnesium (Mg) / platinum (Pt) / zinc (Zn).
Q7 a)   oxygen
b)   aluminium
c)   calcium
d)   chlorine
e)   sodium
f)   fluorine
Q8   All of the substances are elements because they each contain only one type of atom.
Q9 a)   Silicon is a non-metal.
b)   Chlorine is a non-metal.
c)   Oxygen as all the others are in the same group.
d)   Hydrogen as all the others are in the same group.
e)   Iron as all the others are in the same group.
f)   Lithium is the only metal.
Q10 a)   The second sentence should be crossed.
b)   Elements in the same period have **different** properties to each other.
Q11 a)   Group 1
b)   E.g. soft, shiny
c)   They change.
d)   The elements at the bottom react more violently than those at the top.
e)   It fizzes a lot and catches fire — potassium
It fizzes a lot — sodium
It fizzes a bit — lithium

Pages 15-17 Compounds
Q1 a)   There must be atoms of at least two different elements in a compound, molecules are formed when atoms join together.
b)   A chemical bond.
Q2   Elements — sulfur, lead, oxygen, helium, calcium, chlorine
Compounds — magnesium oxide, sodium chloride, water, carbon dioxide, sulfur dioxide, carbon monoxide, sulfuric acid
Q3 a)   A and C, because the atoms that make up the molecules are different.
b)   B, because the atoms are all the same.
Q4 a)   FeS
b) O_2
c)   HCl
d) N_2
e) H_2O

f) CO_2
Q5 a)   iron (Fe) and sulfur (S)
b)   sodium (Na) and chlorine (Cl)
c)   carbon (C) and oxygen (O)
Q6 a)   one
b)   four
c)   two
Q7   In a **chemical reaction**, chemicals join together or split apart to form new **substances**. When elements **combine** like this, they form new **compounds**. Compounds produced in a chemical reaction will have **different** properties to the original elements. For example, **iron** is magnetic. When it reacts with **sulfur**, it makes **iron sulfide** which **isn't** magnetic.

Pages 18-20 — Mixtures
Q1   A substance made up of only one type of element or only one type of compound.
Q2 a)   A and C
b)   C
c)   B
Q3 a)   true
b)   true
c)   false
d)   false
e)   true
Q4 a)   Two or more substances that are not chemically joined up.
b)   The mixture, because the compound can only be separated with a chemical reaction/the elements in the mixture are not chemically joined.
Q5   A solid being dissolved is called a **solute**.
A liquid that a solid is being dissolved into is called a **solvent**.
The mixture of a dissolving solid and liquid is called a **solution**.
A solid that will dissolve is called **soluble**.
A solid that won't dissolve is called **insoluble**.
Q6   E.g. she could heat the beaker until the water evaporates.
Q7 a)   The salt has not vanished, it has been **dissolved** in the water.
b)   They break.
c)   E.g.

Q8 a)   E.g. the sugar particles fill the gaps between the water particles.
b)   84 g

Pages 21-24 — Separating Mixtures
Q1 a)   E.g. salt is soluble in water but sand isn't.
b)   1 — grinding
2 — dissolving
3 — filtering
4 — evaporating
c)   E.g. the sand doesn't dissolve in water and stays as big grains. The big grains don't fit through the tiny holes in the filter paper.

Answers

d) Because it dissolves in the water and goes through the filter paper.
e) salt crystals
Q2 a) distillation
b) The water in saltwater boils off and is collected in the beaker.
c) To cool the water so that it condenses from a gas into a liquid and can be collected.
d) E.g. dirty water
e) In the flask before the experiment — a mixture of water and salt particles.
In the flask after the experiment — just salt particles.
In the beaker after the experiment — just water particles.
Q3 a) C, F, D, A, E, B
b) chromatography
Q4 a) Lola and Paul
b) Paul's ink and the Lola's ink were both made up of two dyes and the results show these dyes travelled the same amount along the filter paper — they're probably the same ink.
Q5 a) The water was pure.
b) The water contained impurities because it boiled above the normal boiling point.

Pages 25-27 — Properties of Metals
Q1 All the elements to the left of the zigzag should be shaded.
Q2 They are good conductors of heat.
Q3 These should be circled: cobalt, nickel, iron anchor.
Q4 a) i) smooth
ii) They reflect light well.
b) i) Although the fire made the gong very **hot**, the brass gong didn't melt because metals have **high** melting points. The atoms in metals are joined up with **strong** bonds. That means a lot of **heat** energy is needed to break the bonds between metal atoms.
ii) E.g. metals conduct heat, so they let heat energy pass through them easily. So the heat will travel from one side of the gong to the other.
c) They are sonorous.
Q5 a) They are ductile.
b) They are good conductors of electricity.
c) E.g. non-metals are brittle / don't conduct electricity.
d) Casing that protects you from the electricity flowing in the plug.
Q6 a) easily shaped
b) Metals are very dense because they have a lot of atoms in a small space.

Pages 28-30 — Properties of Non-Metals
Q1

B	C	N	O	F	Ne
Al	Si	P	S	Cl	Ar
Ga	Ge	As	Se	Br	Kr
In	Sn	Sb	Te	I	Xe
Tl	Pb	Bi	Po	At	Rn

Q2 They have low densities

Q3 Non-metals have **low** melting points and **low** boiling points. This is because the forces which hold the particles together are very **weak**.
Q4 The iron barrel could be lifted out.
Q5 1 — Non-metal
2 — Metal
Q6 a) carbon
b) It breaks.
c) Non-metals are brittle.
d) The graphite in a pencil wears away **quickly**. This is because the **structure** of graphite is **weak** so the rough surface of the paper **scrubs away bits of** the graphite.
Q7 a) Test A is testing **whether the substance conducts electricity**.
The mystery substance in this test is probably a **non-metal** because **it doesn't conduct electricity**.
b) Test B is testing **whether the substance bends/is malleable**.
The mystery substance in this test is probably a **non-metal** because **it is brittle**.
c) Test C is testing **the melting point of the substance**.
The mystery substance in this test is probably a **non-metal** because **it has a low melting point**.
d) Test D is testing **whether the substance is magnetic**.
The mystery substance in this test is probably a **metal** because **it is magnetic**.

Pages 31-33 — Properties of Other Materials
Q1 a) E.g. they are stiff / they are insulators of heat.
b) E.g. they can withstand large forces before breaking / they don't let the tea lose a lot of heat.
c) E.g. plates/ornaments
Q2 a) Strong but not heavy
b) A trombone should be strong so that it doesn't break, but should not be heavy as it has to be held to be played.
c) E.g. plastic bags/canoes
Q3

Bone china — C	Porcelain — C
PVC — P	Polythene — P
Nylon — P	Glass — C

Q4 Because ceramics are insulators of heat.
Q5 a) A material made from two or more different materials stuck together.
b) They have properties that are more useful than the properties of the materials they are made up of.
c) Fibreglass is made from **glass** fibres mixed into **plastic**. This means it has **properties** of both materials. Fibreglass has a **low** density, like plastic, but it is very **strong** like glass.
d) E.g. skis, surfboards.
Q6 a) A composite material.
b) Sand, gravel and cement should be ticked.
c) It can cope with being squashed without breaking, so it's good at supporting heavy things.
Q7 a) Polymers

10

Answers

b) E.g. Feature 1 — polymers can be easily moulded, so the kettle can be shaped like a gnome.
Feature 2 — polymers are very lightweight for their size.

Section 2 — Chemical Changes
Pages 34-35 — Equations
Q1 a) In a chemical reaction, chemicals **combine** or **split** to form **new** substances.
b) products
c) nitric acid and sodium hydroxide
Q2 a) The periodic table
b) The formula for a compound is made up of the symbols of the elements inside it.
c) C, H, Fe, O and Na should be ticked.
Q3 a) i) carbon dioxide
ii) sodium chloride
b) i) H_2O
ii) two
iii) one
Q4 a) hydrochloric acid + sodium hydroxide → sodium chloride + water
b) $HCl + NaOH \rightarrow NaCl + H_2O$

Page 36 — Chemical Reactions
Q1 Atoms **are not** made or destroyed in a chemical reaction. The atoms **move around** during a chemical reaction and **are not** changed.
Q2 a) 200 g
b) i) E.g. a gas/solid being made.
ii) Atoms are never made in a chemical reaction.
c) It is the same as the total mass of the reactants.

Pages 37-39 — Examples of Chemical Reactions
Q1 Fuel, heat and oxygen.
Q2 a) orange/brown
b) iron + oxygen → **iron oxide**
c) The reaction of the nail and oxygen is an **oxidation** reaction. This reaction of iron and oxygen is also called **rusting**.
d) The air.
Q3 Combustion releases energy.
Q4 a) hydrogen and carbon
b) hydrocarbon + oxygen → carbon dioxide + water
c) A bonfire
Q5 a) combustion
b) heat and light
c) carbon dioxide / water vapour
Q6 a) Oxidation is when a substance reacts with and gains oxygen.
b) Combustion should be circled.
Q7 a) thermal decomposition
b) carbon dioxide
c) Only certain substances break down when they are heated.
d) copper carbonate → copper oxide + carbon dioxide

Pages 40-41 — More on Chemical Reactions
Q1 a) This reaction **gave out** energy.

b) heat
c) exothermic
Q2 a) True
b) False
c) False
d) True
Q3 thermal decomposition
Q4 Endothermic — sports injury cold packs
Exothermic — hand warmers, self-heating cans of coffee and a fire burning
Q5 a) A catalyst is a substance that speeds up a reaction.
b) You can make **more** product in the **same** amount of time by using a catalyst in a reaction. Catalysts can also allow reactions to happen at **lower** temperatures, which makes reactions **cheaper**.
c) Yes, catalysts don't get used up or changed in a reaction.

Pages 42-43 — Acids and Alkalis
Q1 Soap — alkaline
Lemon — acidic
Lemonade — acidic
Bleach — alkaline
Water — neutral
Washing powder — alkaline
Q2 Strong alkali — pH 14
Neutral — pH 7
Strong acid — pH 1
Weak alkali — pH 9
Weak acid — pH 5
Q3 Indicator
Q4

Useful Substance	typical pH value	Colour with Universal Indicator	Acidic, Alkaline or Neutral
a) Hydrochloric acid in stomach	1	red	strong acid
b) Rain water	5	yellow	weak acid
c) Sodium hydroxide (oven cleaner)	13	purple	strong alkali
d) Tap water	7	green	neutral
e) Washing up liquid	8	blue	weak alkali

Q5 Litmus paper is an indicator.
Universal indicator can be used to work out the pH of a solution.
Citric acid is a stronger acid than rain water.

Pages 44-45 — Neutralisation Reactions
Q1 a) False
b) True
c) True
d) False
Q2 a) acid + alkali → salt + water
b) neutralisation
c) pH 7
Q3 Hydrochloric acid — calcium chloride, potassium chloride.
Sulfuric acid — sodium sulfate, calcium sulfate, magnesium sulfate
Q4 a) i) 1. Fill a test tube with 20 cm³ of sodium hydroxide.

Answers

2. Add a few drops of hydrochloric acid to the test tube.

3. Take a small sample of the solution in the test tube to see if the pH is neutral.

4. Repeat the last two steps until you have a neutral solution.

5. Add the solution to a dish and boil off some of the liquid so you're left with a concentrated solution.

6. Leave the solution over night to form nice big salt crystals.

ii) water

b) E.g. wear eye protection.

c) hydrochloric acid + sodium hydroxide → **sodium chloride** + water

Pages 46-47 — Reactivity Series and Metal Extraction

Q1
1 — potassium
2 — magnesium
3 — aluminium
4 — zinc
5 — iron
6 — copper

Q2 a) lead — reduced by carbon
potassium — electricity
magnesium — electricity

b) A metal can be extracted from its ore using carbon if it is **less** reactive than carbon.

Q3 a) The process of extracting a metal from its ore using carbon is called reduction.

b) Because it is unreactive.

Q4 a) removing oxygen

b) Rocks containing metal compounds (usually metal oxides).

c) carbon + iron oxide → iron + carbon dioxide

d) Aluminium is higher than carbon in the reactivity series / is more reactive than carbon.

e) electricity

Pages 48-50 — Reaction of Metals with Acids

Q1 potassium, sodium and calcium

Q2 a)

Metal	Observations of reaction	Sound made by a lit splint above reaction
zinc	Reacted fairly well	Squeaky pop
magnesium	Reacted violently	Big squeaky pop
iron	Reacted fairly well	Small squeaky pop
copper	Didn't react	No sound

h) Hydrogen

Q3 a) 5 cm³

b) More violent, because calcium is higher than aluminium in the reactivity series.

Q4 a) They would react violently.

b) A (big) squeaky pop.

c) A salt

Q5 a) potassium sulfate + hydrogen

b) sodium chloride + hydrogen

c) iron sulfate + hydrogen

d) No reaction — metal too unreactive.

e) magnesium sulfate + hydrogen

Q6

The mystery word is reaction.

Pages 51-52 — Reactions of Oxides with Acids

Q1 a) iron oxide

b) water

c) aluminium oxide

d) carbon dioxide

Q2 a) oxygen

b) potassium

c) oxygen, sulfur

d) lead, oxygen

Q3 a) alkali

b) lithium chloride

c) water

Q4 a) A non-metal oxide

b) acidic

c) water and salt

Q5
1 — Non-metal
2 — Salt
3 — Alkali
4 — Sodium
5 — Metal
6 — Acid
7 — Lithium

Pages 53-55 — Displacement Reactions

Q1 a)

Original metal	Deposited Metal
Magnesium	Copper
Copper	No deposit
Iron	Copper

b) i) iron + copper sulfate → **copper** + **iron** sulfate

ii) displacement

c) copper

d) No change. Silver is less reactive than copper and will not displace it.

Q2 a)

Metal	Reaction with iron sulfate
Magnesium	✔
Aluminium	✔
Iron	✗
Lead	✗
Copper	✗

b) zinc

Q3 a) magnesium

b) iron

Answers

c) lead
d) reactive
e) colourless
f) iron
The mystery metal is silver.
Q4 a) Metal X is less reactive than **iron** and more reactive than **copper**.
b) E.g. lead
c) 1 — magnesium, 2 — iron, 2 — metal X, 4 — copper
Q5 a) hydrogen
b) sodium

Section 3 — The Earth and The Atmosphere
Pages 56-57 — The Earth's Structure
Q1 a)

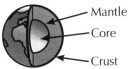

Mantle
Core
Crust

b) The Earth is almost a **sphere** and is made up of several layers. The **crust** is a thin layer of solid **rock**. The core is at the **centre** of the Earth.
c) The mantle is mostly **solid**, but deep down it can flow very **slowly** like a **liquid**.
d) i) crust
ii) core
Q2 a) rocks ➡ **minerals** ➡ **compounds** and **elements**
b) E.g. quartz
Q3 a) The upper mantle and the crust.
b) i) They 'float' on the mantle.
ii) Slowly.
c) Plates moving very suddenly.

Pages 58-60 — Rock Types
Q1 There are **three** different types of rock. Igneous rocks are formed when melted underground rock called **magma** cools. Sedimentary rocks are formed from layers of sediment laid down in lakes or **seas** over **millions** of years. The particles of sediment are stuck together by other **minerals**. Sometimes the remains of long dead plants and animals are found in the rock. These are called **fossils**. Metamorphic rocks are formed by heat and pressure acting on existing rocks over **long** periods of time. Metamorphic rocks can contain tiny **crystals** and may also have **layers**.
Q2 a) It is pushed out through volcanoes.
b) Magma below the ground can cool to form igneous rocks.
Q3 Basalt — **I**
Chalk — **S**
Slate — **M**
Grit — **S**
Granite — **I**
Marble — **M**
Obsidian — **I**
Sandstone — **S**

Quartzite — **M**
Q4 a) Layers of sediment are laid down over millions of years and stuck together by other minerals.
b) It formed from magma pushing up into the crust and cooling.
c) Metamorphic rock
d) Heat and pressure

Pages 61-62 — The Rock Cycle
Q1 a) uplift
b) melting
c) cooling
d) erosion
e) exposure
f) heat and pressure
g) weathering
h) deposition
i) burial and compression
j) transportation
Q2 a) true
b) true
c) true
d) true
e) false
f) true
g) false
Q3

Label	Number
Sedimentary rocks	7
Metamorphic rocks	8
Sediments	5
Magma	10
Weathering	2
Erosion and transport	3
Igneous rock	11
Deposition	4
Exposure	1
Melting	9
Burial and compression	6

Pages 63-64 — Recycling
Q1 a) plastic bags, petrol, plastic cups
b) Millions of years ago, dead **plants** and animals were buried in the Earth's crust. Over time, they turned into fossil fuels like **crude oil**. Fossil fuels are **limited** resources because they take such a **long** time to make. Once all the fossil fuels have been used, we won't get any more for **millions of years**.
Q2 a) Taking old or unwanted products and using the materials to make new things.
b) Any three from: It uses fewer limited resources. / It uses less energy, which saves money. / It uses less energy so less fossil fuels are burnt. / It makes less rubbish.
Q3 a) It's usually cheaper to **recycle** materials rather than throwing them away and **making** new ones. It also costs money to send used aluminium to **landfill**. Recycling is generally much more **efficient** than making new materials all the time.

Answers

b) ores

c) i) Fossil fuels will run out faster.

ii) Recycled aluminium. If it wasn't recycled it would have to be mined, extracted and transported, which both use a lot of energy.

iii) Recycled aluminium.

Pages 65-66 — The Carbon Cycle

Q1 a) Carbon is a part of all **living** things. It is never **used up**, just **recycled**. It constantly passes between living things before being returned to the **environment**.

b) photosynthesis

c) plants

Q2 a) carbon dioxide

b) i) E.g. they break down dead organisms and waste.

ii) E.g. when they respire, they return carbon to the air in carbon dioxide.

c) By combustion / by burning them.

Q3 a)

grass   lamb

b) When the grass is eaten by the lamb, the carbon in it goes into the lamb.

Q4

Label	Number
Combustion	7
Respiration (decomposers)	5
Decomposers	4
Photosynthesis	1
Respiration (plants and animals)	2
Fossil fuels	6
Eating	3

Pages 67-68 — The Atmosphere and Climate

Q1 a) Gas A — Nitrogen
        Gas B — Oxygen

b) i) 0.04%

ii) E.g. water vapour

Q2 a) Cutting down trees.

b) Deforestation causes an **increase** in carbon dioxide in the atmosphere. This is because there is **less** photosynthesis, so **less** carbon dioxide is removed from the atmosphere.

Q3 a) E.g. driving a car, making electricity.

b) It traps heat from the Sun and stops a lot of it being lost into space.

c) It's increasing.

Q4 a) global warming

b) The level of carbon dioxide in the Earth's atmosphere is increasing.

c) E.g.
        Effect: Melting of the ice at the North and South poles.
        Explanation: Sea levels could rise, leading to floods.
        Effect: Rainfall patterns could change.
        Explanation: It might be harder for farmers to grow crops.

Physics

Section 1 — Energy and Matter

Page 1 — Energy Stores

Q1 chemical energy store — Energy can be released from this store in a reaction.
    kinetic energy store — Moving objects have energy in this store.
    thermal energy store — Hotter objects have more energy in this store than cooler objects.
    magnetic energy store — Pushing two north poles together transfers energy to this store.
    gravitational potential energy store — An object in a gravitational field has energy in this store.
    elastic potential energy store — A stretched rubber band has energy in this store.
    electrostatic energy store — Two electric charges that attract or repel each other have energy in this store.

Page 2 — Energy Transfer

Q1 b) Energy is being transferred to the surroundings' **thermal** energy store.
        Energy is being transferred from the match's **chemical** energy store.

c) Energy is being transferred to the box's **gravitational potential** energy store.
        Energy is being transferred from the box's **kinetic** energy store.

d) Energy is being transferred to the battery's **chemical** energy store.
        Energy is being transferred from the handle's **kinetic** energy store.

Q2 a) 2

b) 1

c) 3

Page 3 — Energy Transfer

Q1 a) by sound, mechanically

b) chemical energy store

c) By heating.

d) Through chemical processes inside the body.

Q2 The knight applies **a force** to make the boulder move. Energy in the knight's **chemical** energy store is transferred to the **kinetic** energy store of the boulder.

Q3 smaller

Pages 4-5 — Energy Transfer by Heating

Q1 a) False

b) True

c) True

d) False

e) False

f) True

Q2 When **energy** is transferred between objects of different temperatures, it is transferred from the **hotter** object to the **cooler** object. When the two objects reach **thermal** equilibrium it means they are at the same **temperature**.

Q3 a) Particles in the **plate** vibrate more than the particles in the **ice cube**.

Answers

b) Particles in the **plate** transfer energy to particles in the **ice cube**.
c) The ice cube **gains** energy and starts to **heat up**.
d) The plate **loses** energy and starts to **cool down**.

Q4 a) When an object transfers energy by waves to the surroundings.
b) The cold drink
c) The cold drink

Q5 a) i) Energy is transferred from the pan to the soup because the pan is **hotter** than the soup.
ii) Energy is transferred from the pan to Rachael's hand slowly because the plastic handle is **an insulator**.
b) To stop the hand getting hot / burnt.

Page 6 — Conservation of Energy

Q1 Energy can never be **created** / **destroyed** nor **destroyed** / **created**, but is only **transferred** from one store to another. This means that energy is **conserved**.

Q2 a) no
b) thermal energy store
c) wasted energy

Q3 Input energy is transferred **electrically** from the mains.
Energy is transferred usefully **by light and sound** from the TV.
Wasted energy is transferred **by heating**.

Q4 Energy input
= Useful energy + Wasted energy
= 2500 + 500 = **3000 J**

Page 7 — Energy Resources

Q1 A great deal of the Sun's energy is transferred away by **light**. Some of this reaches the Earth. Plants transfer this energy to chemical energy stores during a process called **photosynthesis**. This energy is then passed on to animals when they eat the plants. When plants and animals **die** they can become buried and over millions of years they are turned into coal, **oil/gas** and **gas/oil**. We call fuels formed in this way **fossil** fuels.

Q2 a) the Sun
b) wind and waves
c) E.g. wood
d) The sun transfers energy **by light** to solar cells. The solar cells then transfer energy **electrically** to devices.

Page 8 — Generating Electricity

Q1 a) chemical energy store
b) thermal energy store
c) electrically

Q2 a) They will run out.
b) Fossil fuels take **millions** of years to make and **a few minutes** to burn. Once we've used them up, **there will be no more**.

Q3 a) They depend on the Sun, so as long as the Sun shines, they won't run out.
b) renewable

Pages 9-10 — The Cost of Electricity

Q1 a) Anything that needs electricity to work.
b) Energy transferred = Power × Time
= 0.4 kW × 2 h = **0.8 kWh**
c) Cost = Energy transferred × Price per kWh
= 0.8 kWh × 15p = **12p**

Q2 a) Energy transferred (J) = Power (W) × Time (s)
b) Energy transferred (J)
= Power (W) × Time (s)
= 700 × 90 = **63 000 J**

Q3 a) kilowatt-hours
b) Energy transferred = 9937 – 9927
= **10 kWh**
c) Cost = Energy transferred (kWh) × Price per kWh
= 10 kWh × 19p = **190p** (= **£1.90**)
d) Multiply by 30

Page 11 — Comparing Power Ratings and Energy Values

Q1 The power rating of an appliance tells you how fast it transfers **energy**. The **higher** the power rating, the **higher** the amount of energy transferred in a given time.

Q2 a) kilojoules
b) Choco Cookie Crunch Cereal

Q3 a) Energy transferred = Power × Time
= 1000 W × 60 s
= **60 000 J**
b) Less. It has a lower power rating than toaster B.

Pages 12-13 — Physical Changes

Q1 a) dissolving
b) melting
c) freezing
d) condensing

Q2 The water particles get closer together, the water particles are now able to flow.

Q3 a) Dissolving occurs when a solid mixes with a **liquid** to form a **solution**.
b) reversible
c) no

Q4 a) sublimation
b) It stays the same.
c) A solid turning into a gas is an example of a **physical** change.
d) A physical change is not the same as a chemical change.

Q5 a) condensing
b) They get closer together
c) The density will increase.
d) E.g. evaporation

Pages 14-15 — Movement of Particles

Q1 a) randomly
b) Brownian motion

Q2 a)

Answers

b) All the gas particles move around at random with **Brownian** motion. The gas B particles eventually bump their way from an area of **high** concentration to an area of **low** concentration. They will constantly bump into each other until they are **evenly** spread out amongst the **gas A** particles.

c) diffusion

Q3 a) As the temperature **increases** the liquid particles start to move around **more** as they have more **energy**. The spaces between the particles get **bigger**, causing the liquid to **expand** and move **up** the thin tube of the thermometer.

b) A - low
B - high

Section 2 — Forces and Motion

Pages 16-17 — Speed

Q1 a) Speed is a measure of how **far** you travel in a set amount of **time**.

b) miles per hour, metres per second, kilometres per hour

Q2 speed = distance ÷ time

Q3 speed = distance ÷ time
= 12 m ÷ 6 s = **2 m/s**

Q4 Speed = Distance ÷ Time
= 700 miles ÷ 2 hours = **350 mph**

Q5 speed

Q6 a) The cat is not moving

b) The cat is moving at a constant speed

c) The cat is travelling back towards its starting point

d) Its speed is increasing

Page 18 — Forces and Movement

Q1 Forces are measured in **newtons** and can be measured using a **newton meter**. They are usually **pushes/pulls** or **pulls/pushes**. They usually act in **pairs**.

Q2 a) True

b) False

c) False

d) True

Q3 Speed up or start moving — hitting a snooker ball
Change direction — a tennis ball bouncing off a wall
Change shape — stretching an elastic band
Turn — unscrewing a bottle lid
Slow down or stop moving — applying the brakes on a bicycle

Pages 19-20 — Friction and Resistance

Q1 a) Friction is a type of **force**.

b) The direction that friction acts is always **opposite to** the direction of movement.

c) To start something moving, the push or pull force must be **bigger** than resisting forces like friction.

d) To push something out of the way, you need to **overcome** friction.

e) There will be **friction** between two objects when their surfaces rub together.

f) Air resistance pushes against objects moving through air to try and **slow them down**.

Q2 a) Weight

b) i) Water resistance

ii) Upwards

Q3 a) Weight

b) Air resistance

c) Force B gets **bigger** as the sky-boarder moves faster.

d) Constant

Q4 a) i) It increases

ii) Because there's now a much larger area trying to cut through the air.

b) It will decrease

Pages 21-22 — Force Diagrams

Q1 a) balanced

b) unbalanced

c) unbalanced

d) balanced

Q2 Shark — unbalanced
Helicopter — balanced
Car — unbalanced

Q3 a) Downwards

b) Reaction

c) Upwards (in the opposite direction to the weight)

d) 35 N

e)

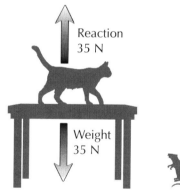

Reaction 35 N

Weight 35 N

Q4 slowing down

Q5 a) Overall force = 700 N – 500 N = **200 N**
The boat is **speeding up**.

b) Overall force = 850 N – 850 N = **0 N**
The skydiver is **moving at a constant speed**.

Q6

Engine Force

22 000 N

2000 N

Pages 23-25 — Moments

Q1 a) i) A moment is a measure of the **turning** effect of a force.

ii) When a force acts on something with a **pivot**, it can create a moment.

iii) Moments are measured in **Nm / newton metres**.

Answers

b)

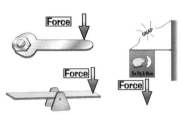

Q2 a) Moment = force × distance
= 20 N × 1 m = **20 Nm**

b) clockwise

Q3 The anticlockwise moments must equal the clockwise moments.

Q4 a) Moment caused by Anna's weight
= force × distance
= **300** N × **2** m
= **600 Nm**

b) Moment caused by Aaron's weight
= force × distance
= **400** N × **2** m
= **800 Nm**

c) The **clockwise** moment due to **Aaron's** weight is greater than the **anticlockwise** moment due to **Anna's** weight, so the seesaw moves **clockwise**.

Q5 a) anticlockwise

b) Moment = force × distance
= 10 N × 0.3 m = **3 Nm**

c) 3 Nm

Q6 The moments created by the dog and the squirrel are no longer balanced. The moment created by the dog has decreased. The seesaw will rotate anticlockwise.

Pages 26-27 — Forces and Elasticity

Q1 a) i) Changing the shape of an object.
  ii) A force

b) Any object that can be stretched or compressed and return to its original shape

c) E.g. a spring

Q2 Dennis **deforms** the elastic by **stretching** it. He is doing **work** because energy is being transferred. Energy is being transferred from his **kinetic** energy store to the **elastic potential** energy store of the elastic. When he releases the elastic, it returns to its original **shape**.

Q3 a) Hooke's Law says that as you increase the force on an object to stretch it, the amount the object is stretched **increases** at **the same** rate.

b) Hooke's Law only applies **up to** a certain force.

c) The force at which Hooke's Law stops working for springs is **higher** than for most other materials.

d) The force and extension of a spring obeying Hooke's Law are **directly** proportional.

Q4 a) 10 N

b) Upwards (in the opposite direction to the weight).

c) The forces on the spring are in **equilibrium**.

Pages 28-31 — Pressure

Q1 a) The force over a certain area

b) The more **force** there is over a given **area**, the **greater** the pressure.

Q2 Pressure = force ÷ area

Q3 If a force of 1 **N** is spread over an **area** of 1 m^2, then it exerts a **pressure** of 1 **Pa** .

Q4 75 Pa

Q5 0.6 N/m^2

Q6 a) 20 N

b)

Base area
18 m^2

Q7 a) 0.25 m^2 + 0.25 m^2 + 0.25 m^2 + 0.25 m^2 = **1 m^2**

b) Pressure = force ÷ area
= 30 000 N ÷ 1 m^2 = **30 000 N/m^2**

Q8 As the balloon gets higher there is **less** atmosphere above it so the weight of the atmosphere pressing down on it **decreases**. The area of the balloon that this weight is acting on **stays the same** and so the atmospheric pressure on the balloon **decreases**.
When the balloon loses height there is **more** atmosphere above it. The weight of the atmosphere pressing down on it **increases** and so the atmospheric pressure on the balloon **increases**.

Q9 a) True

b) True

c) False

d) True

Q10 a) upthrust

b) The force caused by water pressure pushing upwards at the bottom of the submarine is **bigger than** the force caused by water pressure pushing down at the top of the submarine.

Q11 Duck — float
Book — sink
Apple — float

Q12 The area of the sharp pin end is much smaller than the flattened end. So when the force is applied, the pressure is greater in case 1 and so the pin is pushed into the board.

Section 3 — Waves
Pages 32-33 — Water Waves

Q1 a) Water waves are a type of **transverse** wave. The undulations of the water wave are **at right-angles to** the direction that the wave is travelling in.

b) i) energy
  ii) In the same direction that the wave is travelling in.

c) The wave will be reflected / it will change direction.

d)

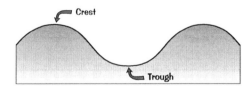

Q2 a) i) B
  ii) A

b) The crest and trough would cancel each other out.

Answers

Pages 34-35 — Light Waves
Q1 a) An object that produces light.
b) the Sun, a light bulb, a flame.
Q2 a) Light always travels in a **straight** line.
We can see because light produced by **luminous** objects is **reflected** off other objects and into our **eyes**.
b) E.g.

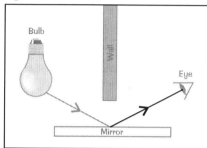

Accept any answer that shows the light ray travelling in a straight line from where it hits the mirror's surface to the pupil of the eye.
Q3 a) Both
b) Both
c) Both
d) Light only
e) Both
Q4 a) Light waves **don't need** particles to travel, but water waves **do**. There **aren't any** particles in a vacuum, so water waves **can't** travel though them, but light waves **can**.
b) i) Vacuum
ii) Light waves are **slowed down by** particles.
c) 300 000 000 m/s

Pages 36-37 — Reflection
Q1 a) The light is reflected off the object / changes direction.
b) Light is only reflected off mirrors. — False
Light is not reflected off objects with a rough surface. — False
Light is only reflected off objects with a shiny surface. — False
Light is reflected off most objects. — True
Q2 a) Mirrors have a very **smooth** shiny surface. When light hits a mirror at an angle, all the light is **reflected** at the **same** angle, giving a clear reflection. This is known as **specular** reflection.
b) i) It is reflected in lots of different directions / the light is scattered.
ii) diffuse scattering
Q3 a) Angle of incidence = angle of reflection.
b)

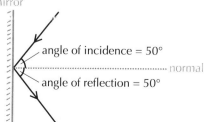

(You could also have drawn the light ray travelling the same path but in the opposite direction. In that case the angle of incidence and angle of reflection would be drawn the other way round.)

Pages 38-40 — Refraction
Q1 a) Any substance that light or sound travels though is called a medium.
b) When light moves from one medium into another, its speed **is** changed. If the light enters the new medium at an angle, it **bends**. This happens because the speed of light is **different** in different materials. The name given to this effect is **refraction**.
Q2 a) opaque
transparent
b) T (transparent): jam jar, window, wine glass, water, glasses lens.
O (opaque): wall, brick, sheep, tree.
Q3 a) D
b) The light ray hits the glass straight on.
Q4 When light travels from a more dense medium to a less dense medium, the light rays bend **away from** the normal.
When light travels from a less dense medium to a more dense medium, the light rays bend **towards** the normal.
Q5 E.g.

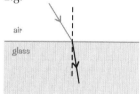

Accept any answer which shows the ray bent towards the normal.
Q6 a) B
b) The light ray from the torch **speeds up** when it leaves the water.
Q7

	T	R	A	N	S	P	A	R	E	N	T
		D	E	N	S	E					
	R	E	F	R	A	C	T				
			R	A	Y						
			A	W	A	Y					
	I	N	C	I	D	E	N	T			
			T	O	W	A	R	D	S		
M	E	D	I	U	M						
			O	P	A	Q	U	E			
			N	O	R	M	A	L			

Pages 41-44 — Lenses and Cameras
Q1 a) A — Tracing paper
B — The object being viewed
C — Pinhole
b) Light travels in **straight** lines from the object being viewed through the **pinhole** towards the **tracing paper**. The pinhole is very **small**, so only one **ray** from each point on the object gets into the camera.

Answers

c)   E.g.

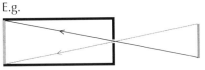

d) i)

ii)   Because the rays of light cross over inside the camera.

Q2   1 — Light from the Sun is reflected by objects towards our eyes.
2 — The cornea of each eye focuses most of the incoming light.
3 — Light is focused further by the lens.
4 — An image is formed on the retina.

Q3   An image formed on the eye's retina will be **upside down** because the light rays cross over.

Q4 a) i)   retina
ii) cornea
iii) lens

b)

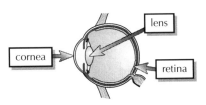

Q5 a)   refraction
b)   E.g.

Q6 a)   Anything that absorbs energy.
b)   energy
c)   retina cell in the eye
film in a film camera
sensor in a digital camera

Q7   When light enters the eye, **energy** is transferred to the eye's **retina** by the light, causing **electrical / chemical** and **chemical / electrical** changes in cells at the back of the eye. These changes cause signals to be sent to the **brain**.

When light enters a digital camera, **energy** is transferred to the camera's **sensor** by the light, causing it to produce an **electrical** charge. Changes in charge are read by a **computer** and turned into a digital image.

Page 45 — Light and Colour

Q1 a)   Light from the Sun and light bulbs is often called **white** light.
b)   Light can be split into its colours using a **prism**.
c)   This splitting is called **dispersal**.

d)   The pattern of colours made like this is called a **spectrum**.

Q2 a) i)   violet
ii) A — red, B — orange, C — yellow, D — green, E — blue, F — indigo, G — violet

b) i)   Different colours are caused by light waves having different **frequencies**.
ii) Red light has a **lower** frequency than violet light.
iii) The number of **waves** of light that pass a point per second is called the frequency.

Pages 46-48 — Absorption and Reflection of Colour

Q1 a)   A post box is red because the paint on it **reflects** red light and **absorbs** all the other colours. A dandelion flower appears yellow because it absorbs **all** the colours of light except for **yellow**.

b) i)   All colours.
ii) All colours.

Q2 a) i)   red
ii) they are absorbed

b)

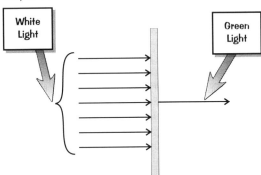

Q3 a) i)   The cube will absorb the light that is **not red** and reflect the light that is **red**.
ii) red

b) i)   black
ii) The cube absorbs all the green light so no light is reflected.

c)   green

Q4 a)   At night, the only light on the street is orange. An **orange** car or a **white** car would reflect all of the orange light, so it would appear **orange**. A **blue** car would absorb all of the orange light, so it would appear **black**.

b)   blue — blue
orange — orange
white — white

c)   **White** light is better than **orange** light for street lights because everything appears **its actual colour** in white light.

Pages 49-50 — Sound

Q1 a)   True
b)   False
c)   True

Q2 a) i)   The vibrations in longitudinal waves are **parallel** to the direction of the wave.
ii) The vibrations in longitudinal waves are **parallel** to the direction of energy transfer.

b)   sound waves, waves on a slinky pushed at the end

Answers

Q3 a) There were no particles inside the jar, and sound needs particles to travel.
b) i) It's soft.
ii) E.g. curtains, carpets.
Q4 Sounds travel through **mediums**. When something vibrates, it passes on the sound **vibrations** to the particles next to it. These vibrations are then passed through the medium as a series of **compressions** — areas of squashed-up particles.
Q5 a) i) Light
ii) Russell **saw** the explosion before he **heard** it.
b) The sound waves travelling through the ground.
c) Sound waves being reflected off a surface.

Pages 51-53 — Hearing
Q1 a) Frequency is the number of **waves** per second.
b) Frequency is a measure of **pitch**.
c) A **high** frequency means a high-pitched sound.
d) Frequency is measured in **hertz**.
Q2 A — ear flap
B — ear drum
C — ear bones
D — auditory nerve
E — cochlea
Q3 a) 100 000 Hz
b) 25 Hz
Q4 a) i) 40 000 Hz
ii) bottlenose dolphin
iii) bottlenose dolphin
b) i) 20 Hz to 20 000 Hz
ii) The bottom string on a guitar, a person talking.
Q5 2 — The vibrations of the drum surface are passed to the air particles.
4 — The ear drum vibrates.
7 — A message is sent to the brain.
5 — The ear bones vibrate.
3 — The air particles vibrate.
1 — The surface of the drum vibrates.
6 — Hairs in the cochlea vibrate.

Pages 54-56 — Energy and Waves
Q1 When **waves** transfer energy from one place to another, they can also transfer **information**. Sound waves do this through **vibrations** between **particles**. This is useful for **recording** and replaying sounds.
Q2 a) 1 — E.g. thin paper
2 — E.g. thin plastic sheet
b) E.g. as sound waves / by vibrating the particles in the air.
c) The **vibrations** in a sound wave make the diaphragm vibrate inside the microphone. The microphone turns the vibrations into **electrical signals**.
d) loudspeaker.
Q3 B ➡ E ➡ A
Q4 Ultrasound is **high** frequency sound that is outside the normal auditory range of humans. Humans **can't** hear ultrasound **at all**.

Q5 a) **Vibrations** from the ultrasound **waves** remove dirt from the object, leaving it **clean**.
b) E.g. false teeth and jewellery.
Q6 a) E.g. because ultrasound waves can reach deep inside your body.
b) i) Make sure both people have pain in the same muscle, make sure the people are about the same age.
ii) B — Ultrasound physiotherapy didn't have any effect on muscle pain.
iii) Use a bigger sample, repeat the experiment.

Section 4 — Electricity and Magnetism
Pages 57-58 — Electrical Circuits
Q1 a) false
b) true
c) false
Q2

Q3 a) The flow of charge around a circuit.
b) The current in a circuit **does not get** used up as it flows round the circuit.
Q4 a) potential difference
b) The current will increase.
Q5 a) Resistance slows down the flow of current.
b) ohms
c) insulators
Q6 a) Material A
b) Resistance is equal to the potential difference divided by the current.
c) Material B

Pages 59-60 — Measuring Current and Potential Difference
Q1 a) amperes / amps
b) ammeter
c) 2 A
Q2 a) voltmeter
b) volts
c)

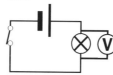

Q3 a) The battery will supply a potential difference of 12 V.
b) No, the potential difference across the bulb needs to be 5 V or less.
Q4
Switch (open) ─o̶ ̶o─
Switch (closed) ─o─o─
Bulb ─⊗─
Ammeter ─(A)─
Battery ─┤|┆|┆|├─
Cell ─┤├─

Answers

Q5 E.g.

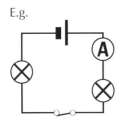

Pages 61-63 — Series and Parallel Circuits

Q1 The current can only travel one way around the circuit. The current gives up some of its energy to the bulb.

Q2 a) Series because e.g. the current has no choice of route.

b) E.g.

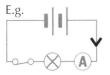

c) 2 A

Q3 None of them

Q4 a) T
b) F
c) T
d) F

Q5 a) The current splits. / The current is divided between each branch.

b)

Change to original circuit	Bulb(s) on	Bulb(s) off
Bulb A is unscrewed	B, D, E	A, C
Bulb D is unscrewed	A, C, E	B, D
Bulb E is unscrewed		A, B, C, D, E

Q6 a) i) 10 A
ii) 9 A

b) E.g. If one bulb blows, the other bulb will stay lit. If they were wired in series, then if one bulb were to blow they would both go out. / In a parallel circuit you can turn one light off without having to turn both lights off. In a series circuit you have to turn both lights on and off together.

Q7

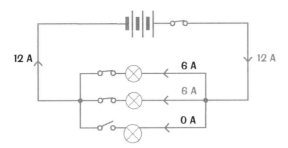

Pages 64-66 — Static Electricity

Q1 a) Atoms contain positive and negative **charges**.
b) Electrons are the **negative** parts of atoms.
c) **Electrons** can move, but **positive charges** can't.
d) Electrons can be **transferred** when two insulating objects are rubbed together.
e) When an object gains electrons, it becomes **negatively** charged.

f) An object that **loses** electrons is left with a positive charge.

Q2 a) **Electrons** are scraped off the **cloth** and left on the **rod**.
b) i) False
ii) True
iii) True
iv) False

Q3 a) Charged objects don't need to touch each other to feel a force.

b)

Charge of object 1	Charge of object 2	Force between objects
Positive	Positive	Repulsion
Positive	Negative	Attraction
Negative	Positive	Attraction
Negative	Negative	Repulsion

c) Opposite charges **attract**, charges of the same type **repel**.

Q4 a) static charge
b) E.g. Only negative charges / electrons can move. Negative charges moved from the carpet to the soles of his shoes.

Q5 a) An area around a charged object where other charged objects will feel a force.

b) E.g.

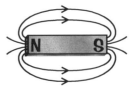

c) The charge on Nena's hair is the **opposite** type as the charge on the balloon. This means the hair is **attracted to** the balloon.
d) Each hair has a positive charge, so they repel each other.

Pages 67-68 — Magnets

Q1 a) bar magnet
b) magnetic field lines
c) The region where magnetic materials experience a force.
d)

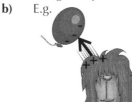

Q2 Unless it is next to a magnet, a compass will **line up** with the Earth's **magnetic** field. The compass will point to the Earth's magnetic **North pole**. **Maps** always show which direction is **north** on them, so you can use them with a compass to find your way.

Q3 a) i) false
ii) true
iii) false
iv) true

Answers

b) Magnets **do not need to** touch for there to be a force between them.

Q4 a) From the North pole of the magnet to the South pole of the magnet, along the magnetic field lines.

b) E.g.

Pages 69-71 — Electromagnets

Q1 Electric current going through a wire causes a magnetic field around the wire.

Q2 a) bar magnet

b) The magnetic field would disappear / be turned off.

c) soft iron

Q3 Have more turns on the coil, increase the current in the wire

Q4 Loop of coiled wire — C
Magnet (South pole) — B
Magnet (North pole) — D
Cell — A

Q5 E.g. You can turn the magnetic field of an electromagnet on and off to pick up and drop the metal. The magnetic field of a normal magnet can't be turned off.

Q6 a) C

b) When the switch is closed a **current** flows through the **wire loop**. The wire loop becomes **magnetic**. The loop is already in a **magnetic field** because it is between two **magnets**. This means the loop feels a **force** which makes the loop turn. The propellor is attached to the loop of wire, so it turns as well.

Section 5 — The Earth and Beyond
Pages 72-73 — Gravity

Q1 a) newtons (N)

b) gravity

c) These statements should be ticked: The mass of an object never changes, mass is measured in kilograms, mass is the amount of 'stuff' in an object.

Q2 Anything with mass will attract... **...anything else with mass.**
The Earth and the Moon are... **...attracted to each other.**
The attraction between the Earth and the Sun is bigger than... **...the attraction between the Earth and the Moon.**
Gravitational field strength is... **...how strong gravity is.**
The attraction between two objects because of

their masses... **...is called gravity.**

Q3 The **force** of **gravity** between two objects depends on their masses. The **bigger** their masses are, the **stronger** it will be.

Q4 a) Weight = Mass × Gravitational field strength
= 1000 kg × 10 N/kg = **10 000 N**

b) i) 1000 kg

ii) Weight = Mass × Gravitational field strength
= 1000 kg × 100 N/kg = **100 000 N**

iii) The robot would not work because the wheels can only support 20 000 N before breaking.

Pages 74-75 — The Sun and Stars

Q1 a) a star

b) orbit

c) rough circle

d) Planets don't give out light but stars do.

Q2 a) A galaxy

b) The Sun

c) billions

d) billions

Q3 a) Proxima Centauri is the **second closest** star to the Earth.

b) i) E.g. a light year is how far light travels in one year.

ii) About 4 years

Q4 E.g. Light years are used to measure huge distances between objects in space. They aren't very useful for measuring small distances like your height.

Q5

Pages 76 — Day and Night and the Four Seasons

Q1 a) The Earth spins on its **axis**.

b) It takes a **year** for the Earth to orbit the Sun once.

c) The tilt of the Earth's axis causes the **seasons**.

d) In summer, **days** last longer than **nights**.

e) There are **four** seasons every year.

f) In **summer**, the sunlight is stronger.

g) The days are always shortest in the **winter**.

Q2 a) day time

b) winter

c) northern hemisphere

d) In the summer, the northern hemisphere is tilted towards the Sun. This means we get more hours of sunlight and the sunlight we get is stronger, so we get longer, warmer days.

ISBN 978 1 84146 894 5

9 781841 468945

SFA32

£2.00
(Retail Price)

www.cgpbooks.co.uk